RADIANT MOTHERHOOD

Radiant Motherhood

A Book for Those Who are Creating the Future

By

Marie Carmichael Stopes

Doctor of Science, London ; Doctor of Philosophy,
Munich ; Fellow of University College, London ;
Fellow of the Royal Society of Literature
and the Linnean Society, London

FOURTH EDITION

LONDON

G. P. PUTNAM'S SONS, LTD.

24 BEDFORD STREET, STRAND, W.C. 2

First Edition . . . August 1920
    Reprinted five times
Second Edition . . .November 1922
    Reprinted once
Third Edition . . . October 1923
    Reprinted twice
Fourth Edition . . .November 1925
    Reprinted . . . October 1926
    Reprinted . . . October 1927

TRANSLATIONS
Published

    German
    Czech
    Spanish
    Dutch
    Hungarian
    Danish-Norwegian

Dedicated to young husbands and all who are creating the future

CONTENTS

Contents

APPENDICES

PREFACE

THIS book is written for the same young
people who inspired *Married Love*.
Many of my readers have asked me to
write such a book as this, and I sincerely hope
that it will not disappoint them. Many, many
people have contributed facts which have helped
me to write it. The book, however, is pre-
eminently the work of my baby son and his
father, whose beautiful spirits have been, and
will be, through all eternity united with me in
a burning desire to bring light into dark places.

M. C. S.

Radiant Motherhood

CHAPTER I

The Lover's Dream

So every spirit, as it is most pure,
    And hath in it the more of heauenly light,
So it the fairer bodie doth procure
    To habit in, and it more fairely dight,
    With chearefull grace and amiable sight.
For of the soule the bodie forme doth take:
For soule is forme, and doth the bodie make.
                SPENCER: *An Hymne in honour of Beautie.*

EVERY lover desires a child. Those who imagine the contrary, and maintain that love is purely selfish, know only of the lesser types of love. The supreme love of true mates always carries with it the yearning to perpetuate the exquisite quality of its own being, and to record, through the glory of its mutual creation, other lives yet more beautiful and perfect.

Existence being such a difficult compromise between our dreams and the material facts of

2

the world, this desire may sometimes be thwarted by factors outside itself ; may even be so suppressed as to be invisible in the conduct and unsuspected in the wishes of the lover. Yet the desire to link their lives with the future is deeply woven into the love of all sound and healthy people who love supremely.

It is commonly said that most women marry for children, and not out of a personal love, and there is more truth in this saying than is good for the race. To-day, alas, many women cannot find the perfect and sensitive mate their hearts' desire and they hope in *any* marriage to get children which will mitigate the consequent loneliness of their lives. Sometimes they may, to some extent, succeed, but far less often than they imagine, for that strange and still but little understood force " heredity " steps in, and the son of the tolerated father may grow infinitely more like his physical father than he is like the dear delight his mother dreamed he might be.

Few girls have not pictured in day dreams the joy of holding in their arms their own beautiful babies. No man of their acquaintance, however, may seem fine enough to be their father. Until she has been crushed by experience, or, unless she listens with absolute belief to the depressing information of her elders, each girl believes that her own intense desire for perfection will be the principal factor in creating the beautiful babies of her dreams. Often it seems as though this power were granted, for women sometimes bear lovely children by fathers in whom one may seek in vain for any bodily grace or charm.

The century long working of economic laws based on physical force, the remnants of which still affect us, has resulted in man generally having the selective power and tending to choose for his wife the most beautiful or charming woman that his means allow ; hence hitherto on the whole, the race has been bred from the better and more beautiful women. This has undoubtedly tended to keep the standard of physical form from sinking to the utter degradation which we see in the worst of the slums, and in institutions where live the feeble-minded offspring of inferior mothers who have wantonly borne children of fathers devoid of any realization of what they were doing.

From these avenues of shame and misery, however, I must steer my line of thought, for this book is written pre-eminently for the young, happy and physically well-conditioned pair who mating beautifully on all the planes of their existence, are living in married love.

Whether early in the days of their marriage or postponed for some months or more out of regard for his wife's body and beauty, the hour

will come when the young husband yearning
above her, sees in his wife's eyes the reflection
of the future, and when their mutual longing
springs up to initiate the chain of lives which
shall repeat throughout the ages the bodily,
mental and spiritual beauties of each other,
which each holds so dear. Perhaps in lovers'
talk and exquisite whispers they have spoken
of this great deed on which they are embarking,
and each has voiced that intense yearning which
filled them to see another " with your eyes,
your hair, your smile," living and radiant.
The lovers dream that they will be repeated
in others of their own creation, always young,
running through the ages which culminate in
the golden glories of the millenium.

The dream is so wonderful, the thought that
it pictures in the mind so full of vernal beauty,
light and vigour that, were facts commensurate
with it, its result should spring all ready formed
from between the lips of those who breathed
its possibilities like Minerva from the head of
Jove.

It seems incredible that such splendid dominant designs to fulfil God's purpose should be
hindered, and made to bend and toil through
the hard material facts of the molecular structure
of the world, and that it is only many months
afterwards that the first outward body is given
to this dream, and that then it is in a form

not strong and dancing in lightness and beauty but weak and helpless with many intensely physical necessities which for months and years will require the utmost fostering care or it will be destroyed by material effects, hostile and too strong for it. Yet such is the limitation of our powers of creation. And underneath the intense passion of love and all its rich dreams of beauty is the slow building, chemically molecule by molecule, biologically cell by cell, against obstacles the surmounting of which seems a superhuman feat.

Lovers who are parents give to each other the supremest material gift in the world, a material embodiment of celestial dreams which itself has the further power of vital creation.

In this and all my work, I speak to the normal, healthy and loving in an endeavour to help them to remain normal, healthy and loving, and thus to perfect their lives. So in this book I do not intend to deal with those whose marriages are mistaken ones, or with those who do not know true love. I write for those who having made a love match are passing together through the ensuing and surprising years, and incidentally doing one of the greatest pieces of work which human beings can do during their progress through this world, and that is creating the next generation.

In nature, the consummation of the physical

act of union between lovers generally results in the conception of a new life. We share this physical aspect of mating and the resulting parenthood with most of the woodland creatures. How far many of the lowlier lives are conscious of the future results of their mating unions is a problem in elementary psychology beyond the realm of present knowledge. But that parenthood is the natural result of their union is to-day known, one must suppose, by almost all young couples who wed. I am still uncertain how far the two are *conscious* of this in the early days of their union, when every circumstance encourages that supreme self-centredness of happy youth. Much must depend on the age, and on the previous experience and education of the two ; much also on their relative natures. A profoundly introspective and thoughtful man and woman are more liable than others to be speedily aware of the many interwoven strands of their joint lives, and to live consciously on several planes of existence simultaneously.

The supreme act of physical union as I have shown in my book, *Married Love*, consists fundamentally of three essential and widely differing reactions, having effects in correspondingly different regions. There is (*a*) the intimately personal effect on the internal secretions and general vitality of the individual partaking of that sacrament ; (*b*) there is the social effect of the union of the two in a mutual act in which they must so perfectly blend and harmonize ; and (c) there is the racial result which may lead to the procreation of a new life.

In the early days of the honeymoon, personal passion and the concentrated delight of each in the mate is probably more than sufficient in all its rich complexity to fill the consciousness of the two who are thus united in a life-long comradeship to form that highest unit, the pair. But as education and the conscious control of our lives grow, the young pair who are so blissfully self-centred as not to remember or not to be aware of the racial effects of their acts are probably decreasing in numbers. Among the best of those who marry to-day, the majority only enter upon parenthood or the possibility of parenthood when they feel justified in so doing. The young man who profoundly loves his wife and who considers the future benefit of their child, protects her from accidental conception or from becoming a mother at times when the strain upon her would be too great, or when he is unable to give her and the coming child the necessary care and support. That myriads of children are born without this consideration on the part of their parents applies to the commonalty of mankind, but not to the best.

Often to-day the betrothed young couple

will speak openly and beautifully of the children they hope to have, while others equally full of the creative dream feel it too tender a subject to put into words, and may marry without ever having given expression to the possibility that they will generate through their love yet other lovers.

CHAPTER II

Conceived in Beauty

. . . Here in close recess
With flowers, garlands and sweet smelling herbs,
Espousèd Eve deck'd first her nuptial bed,
And heav'nly choirs the Hymenæan sung,
What day the genial angel to our sire
Brought her in naked beauty more adorn'd,
More lovely than Pandora, whom the Gods
Endow'd with all their gifts . . .
. . . . Into their inmost bower
Handed they went; and, eased the putting off
Those troublesome disguises which we wear,
Straight side by side were laid; nor turn'd, I ween,
Adam from his fair spouse; nor Eve the rites
Mysterious of connubial love refused:

  . . . .

These, lull'd by nightingales, embracing slept,
And on their naked limbs the flowery roof
Shower'd roses, which the morn repaired. Sleep on,
Blest pair, and O! yet happiest if ye seek
No happier state, and know to know no more.
      MILTON : *Paradise Lost.*

IN ancient Sanskrit, there is a work dealing
minutely with love and with the different
forms its expression takes in different
types of people. This has been modified,

added to and re-written by many later authors, and under various names works based on this are to be found in Sanskrit and translated into various Indian dialects.

In these volumes much that is curious, and to Western nations, absurd, is to be found, but also several profound observations which appear to be based on truths generally ignored by us. One of the interesting themes of these very early writers is a recognition and a description of the characteristics of the best and most perfect type of woman, the " Padmini." In addition to describing fully her physical appearance and characteristics, it is observed that she being a child of light and not of darkness, prefers the supreme act of love to take place in the daylight rather than the dark.

In this country, owing to our artificial, over-burdened and over-strained lives, the physical union of lovers is almost always confined to the night time. Crowded as we are in cities and suburban districts, solitude in Nature is almost impossible ; for most, seclusion is only known in a closed room after dark. The Sanskrit writer of the sixth century, however, takes love more seriously than we do, and he describes how for the sacred union serious preparation of beauty should be made—a room or natural arbour decked with flowers ; and for the supreme expression of love (that is the

love between a pair each of the highest and
most perfect type), this should take place in
the light of day and not the darkness of the
night. Even in our present degraded civilization there are some who do realize the
sacredness and the value of the bodily embrace
in the fresh beauty of nature and sunlight.
There must be many beautiful children who
were conceived from unions which took place
under natural conditions of light and open
air radiance. The most spontaneous time for
conception is the summer when our air is mild
and sweet enough for true love in Nature's way.

In an empire where woodland or seaside
solitude is not obtainable by lovers for this
their most sacred function, the distribution of
the population is gravely wrong. It will, however, probably for some time to come be difficult
for those who desire such a profound return
to natural rectitude, to obtain the necessary
security of seclusion amid beautiful surroundings. Therefore, alas, it will in all probability
long remain only possible to most lovers to
ramble together in nature, and then later to
follow the usual course of uniting within their
room.

We do not know enough about ourselves or
the results of our actions, under our present
conditions, to realize to what extent the hour
of conception modifies the quality of the off-

spring.   We only know that the child of lovers
beautiful in mind and body, the child ardently
desired by them, whose coming is prepared
with every beauty which it is in their power
to obtain, is often well worth all the outlay of
love and thought.   Certainly among those personally known to me who have followed the
rather exceptional course I indicate, the children
are remarkable for both physical beauty and
exquisite vitality, balanced with sweetness and
strength of mental and spiritual qualities.

There is an old and in my opinion valuable
view (although it has not been " scientifically
proved ") that the actual hour of conception,
the condition of the parents at the moment
when the germs fuse is one of vital consequences
to the child-to-be.   Scientific proof of this will
be, of course, extraordinarily difficult to discover, but indirectly there do appear to be
some actual data in favour of the converse,
namely that temporary unhealthy states of the
parents result in the conception of children so
inferior as to be markedly and seriously anti-
social.   Forel (*Sexual Question*, 1908) says :—

The recent researches of Bezzola seem to prove that the
old belief in the bad quality of children conceived during
drunkenness is not without foundation. Relying on the Swiss
census of 1900, in which there figure nine thousand idiots
. . . this author has proved that there are two acute annual
maximum periods for the conception of idiots (calculated

from nine months before birth) the periods of carnival and vintage, when the people drink most. In the wine-growing districts, the maximum conception of idiots at the time of vintage is enormous, while it is almost *nil* at other periods.

It is, of course, not always possible to arrange the hour of the union which will lead to conception. And further even when the hour of the union is arranged, nature, to some extent, controls and may modify conditions before conception. Sometimes the fertilization of the egg cell by the sperm cell takes place in the hour of the bodily union of the lovers, sometimes this inner process is delayed by hours or days (see overleaf). Conception is possible in most women at almost any time during the years of potential motherhood, yet there do appear to be several factors which lead to the potential fertility of a woman varying very much from time to time. Some women, for instance, appear to be liable to conceive only for a certain number of days in each month, and these are in general the two or three days immediately following the monthly period and the day or two immediately before. With other women, however, unions on any day of the month may lead to conception, but this depends, possibly, not only on the woman herself but on the vitality and probable length of life of the sperm cells of her husband. This also varies very greatly in individuals. The longest time which the individual sperm has been observed to remain vital after entry into the woman is seventeen days (see Bossi, *N. Arch. d'Obstetr. Gynocol.*, April 1891).

Hence it will be realized that a union arranged to take place under ideal and perfect conditions, perhaps on a holiday into wild and inspiring solitudes, may result as desired in the entry of the sperm into the womb of the woman, and yet the actual fusion of the sperm and egg cell, and the consequent conception may not come to pass until some days later.

Strange it is indeed in this world, in which so much scientific and laborious observation has been devoted to all sorts of irrelevant and trivial subjects, that knowledge of the actual processes of our own fertilization and conception and of the extent of the significance to the future generations of the mode and condition of the union of the parents are almost totally unknown to scientists or doctors, and are disregarded by the majority of the public.

A recent memoir in the French Academy of Science[1] dealing with statistical figures (going back in France, at any rate, so far as 1853) proves that there does seem to be a definite seasonal influence on the power of conception.

[1] Charles Richet, " De la Variation mensuelle de la Natalité," 1916, Comptes rendus Acad. Sciences, Paris, pp. 141–149 and 161–166.

Taking the births for the whole year, it is found they are not equally divided throughout the months, but that a notable maximum of births is found in February and March for most of the countries in the northern hemisphere, the actual maximum of births being from the 15th February to the 15th March, and thus indicating that the maximum of conceptions took place between the 5th May and the 5th June. Richet quotes Bertillon as having established the fact that this maximum of conceptions does not depend on the chance that brides like to be married in the spring, because an identical maximum is found in the illegitimate birthrate. Richet gives many tables of figures, and maintains that the maximum corresponds both in the town and in the country, among the rich and the poor, and among the married and the unmarried, and is, therefore, in his opinion, an actual physiological function :—

C'est que les conditions physiologiques de la maturation de l'ovule et de sa fécondation ne sont pas également favorables dans toutes les periodes de l' année. Par suite d'une ancestrale prédisposition, au moment du printemps, chez la femme, comme chez la plupart des animaux, mais moins nettement que chez eux, la maturation, la chute et la fécondation de l'ovule se font dans des conditions meilleures et plus assurées.

The corresponding maximum for the southern hemisphere arises between August and October.

This natural tendency to produce children according to the season is, to some extent, altered by the conscious and deliberate control of parenthood, which all the more highly civilized countries now find that their better citizens are exerting.

This natural time for conception will, however, tend not to be thwarted by those who are consciously regulating their lives, because from almost every point of view, the summer is the best time in which to experience the joys of love. As the verdant spring is the best time for a baby to be born, the thoughtful mother-to-be will try, other things being equal, to arrange that its birth should take place then, both for her own sake and for that of the child. The weeks of recovery after the strain of the birth are more easily and happily spent lying in the warm sunshine of a spring or summer garden than in the chill of the winter months, and even the actual expense of the birth is reduced when it takes place in the warmth of the spring or early summer when fires and the labour they involve will be saved.

The child too has warm air to surround it on its first introduction to the outer world after its long period of warmth and protection within its mother, and when in a month or two it is able to kick about on the grass, it benefits directly from the rays of the sun and also from the sun-warmed earth.

Various notable men and women, and, in particular, the famous Dr. Trall of America, have held that the actual hour of conception is the one of fate, and that the moods, feelings and conditions of the parents in that hour work more vital magic then than they can do in any succeeding days or weeks. Instinctively, one would like to feel that this is so. Indeed it will take much to *disprove* it, although it is a theme which it is at present impossible to prove, and it must remain always only a personal bias, until thousands of people who view marriage aright will consciously observe and record many things and contribute them to some thinker who will tabulate, correlate and understand them.

Whether the hour of conception affects the child directly or not, the memory of an ardent and wonderful experience in which the pair of lovers consciously surround themselves with beautiful conditions, and deliberately place themselves through their love at the service of God and humanity in the creation of the next generation, must give a vitalizing and joyous memory to both throughout all their lives. This memory being especially connected with the dear child of that union must, therefore, have in this indirect way at any rate a positive racial value.

CHAPTER III

The Gateway of Pain

As when desire, long darkling, dawns, and fires
The mother looks upon the newborn child,
Even so my Lady stood at gaze and smiled
When her soul knew at length the Love it nurs'd.
Born with her life, creature of poignant thirst
And exquisite hunger, at her heart Love lay
Quickening in darkness, till a voice that day
Cried on him, and the bonds of birth were burst.

D. G. ROSSETTI.

THE price of every beauty in this world is in proportion to its quality, even although the payment of the price exacted may be long deferred or may be made in such an intricate and remote form that its connection with the result is overlooked.

As the greatest thing which lovers can give each other is a child, and as none in the world are so great as lovers, the price exacted by Nature for the child of loving and sensitive people is correspondingly heavy.

This statement may apparently conflict with

18

the idea that the joy of bearing a child to the beloved is a woman's consummation of happiness ; yet it does not conflict, because of the deeper truth that the supremest happiness is mysteriously intermingled with self-sacrifice. A young woman whose character is sufficiently beautiful and sensitive to know the highest joys of motherhood—the full delights of human existence and love—will also be sensitive to the varied pains which motherhood will bring. Indeed, in this respect, the poet's saying that " the heart that is soonest awake to the flowers is always the first to be pricked by the thorn " is essentially true.

The radiance of the highest form of motherhood is that of the transfigured saint, hallowed by suffering comprehended and endured, transmuted into a service beyond and above the lower desires of self.

For long, indeed for the many millions of years during which she has shown a motherhood comparable with that of human beings,[1] Nature has essentially trapped and tricked the mother into her motherhood. All the woodland and jungle creatures, the deer or the tiger, the rabbit or the squirrel, grow up through their

[1] By this I mean the motherhood which carries and protects the developed young within the mother's body, unlike that of the lower animals, such as fishes, which leave the eggs to their fate.

brief adolescence into a partial consciousness of delight in themselves and reach the phase of their development in which their own desires urge them to unite with each other. One can scarcely believe that they are conscious of the resulting parenthood which will become a physical fact at a later date, although the training of her cubs by a woodland mother undoubtedly does include handing on, through some speechless communication, of some actual instruction. A similar blind parenthood, but in addition *coerced*, has for many thousands of years been characteristic of a large portion of the human race. Even to-day motherhood is too often blind : the young girl delighting in herself and the fairness of her own body, conscious of the power she wields in social life as a beautiful and attractive creature whom older people pet and please and young men place upon a pedestal, is urged by this natural self-centred delight into accepting through flattery the enjoyment of herself by some chosen mate ; and the later consequences of motherhood are then faced either in amazed astonishment or in open revolt.

Earlier civilizations often dealt with the excessive births resulting from blind or coerced parenthood by destroying the children as infants after birth. This was done directly, and often by her leading citizens, in Greece (one of the

highest forms of civilization ever attained) and
still infanticide direct or indirect goes on among
all the populous races of the world. Where the
value placed on the mother's mental and physical
suffering is low, one may still see motherhood,
not as a fine, voluntary and glorious act of self-
sacrifice from the highest possible motives of
love and service directly to the beloved, and
indirectly to the race, but as the exploitation
of a trapped and helpless sacrifice.

Mothers will say that their babies are their
greatest joys ; one may ask, therefore, how I
can use the word " sacrifice " in connection
with motherhood. The use of the word is
just, and based on truths too generally concealed by those who know them, and far too
generally unknown by those who ought to know
them. Ignorance of their extent has made men
callous, indifferent or ribald towards the profound sacrifices of motherhood.

Few there be, however, who do not know
of the agonizing torments of actual birth. The
Bible is read aloud in churches, and in its
wording there is some recognition of the existence of this agony, although based upon earlier
and simpler civilizations in which the women
were probably better cared for and better fitted
for motherhood than the majority of women are
to-day. Following biblical tradition, the memory
of the agony of birth is generally portrayed

as being wiped out by the supreme joy in the child which follows. To-day, however, this effacement of the anguish is by no means universal, and the abiding horror of the birth is so great that not a few women refuse to bear another child. Then men, who cannot even imagine the experience of child-bearing, denounce such a mother, rate her and hold her up to derision. How little do they realize that in her they may see Nature's working of the laws of evolution (see p. 24).

The torturing agony of birth might so easily have been averted by Nature had the construction of our bodies differed but very slightly from those which we to-day possess in common with most of the higher animals. The human baby when the hour comes for it to sever its connection from its mother, and as an independent individual to venture into the open air of the world, has to make its way through the arched gateway of bone fixed and set by the mother's own requirements as a frame to her own structure. The encircling archway of bone through which the infant has to pass is but three or four inches in diameter. It would have been possible had our evolution taken a different turn for the infant to have made its exit through the soft wall of the mother's body instead of through this fixed and hardened circle of her bone. But for some causes too remote for us at present to discover this was not so, and the essential fact faces us to-day that every infant born naturally must be born through this circle of bone. Moreover if the infant is a well-developed and healthy one, as the ordinary baby of a healthy and beautiful young couple should naturally and rightly be, that infant's head is larger in diameter than the circle of bone through which it has to pass. Its tissues have, therefore, to be squeezed and pressed to mould their shape in order to allow its exit through the orifice, and this must be a slow process, and one which almost always entails great pressure and consequent agony to the mother. Dr. Mary Scharlieb says in *The Welfare of the Expectant Mother* :—

It is, however, scarcely possible that either the public or the profession realizes that one woman dies in child birth for every 250 children born alive. In addition to this we have to remember that the same accidents and diseases which kill the mothers and the babies inevitably cause a still heavier percentage of crippling and invaliding (p. 43).

Twenty-five per cent. and more of the babies conceived and borne die before they reach normal birth. Often they find the journey through the bony archway into the outer world so difficult and arduous a task that they perish in the process of birth, although probably had they been born by Cesarean section, they would have survived and grown into healthy children.

We do not consider what the infant itself in birth may be enduring. The infant is " unconscious," that is to say it carries no memory of these earlier months in its conscious memory as it grows up, but the excessive moulding, particularly of its head, which often has to take place and sometimes takes weeks to right itself, must, one thinks, greatly disturb the little brain, and in my opinion may have a lifelong effect.

I have never heard this aspect of our present problem duly considered. The fact that the increasing brain capacity of civilized man tends ever to give the new born infant a larger head, and tends proportionately to increase the size of the head out of relation to the size of the circle of its mother's bone, has been commented on, and appears to some far seeing thinkers as the possible cause of the ultimate extinction of the human race. Because if we go on developing in the way we are at present doing, ever depending more and more on our brains, and the head of the new born infant tends to increase with the natural development of the brain, the day will come when the birth of a child is absolutely blocked by the relative diameters of its head and of its mother's pelvic bones. If the higher races maintain a dominant place in the world, the day may come when with nearly all women such an incompatible relation will arise. Of what avail then would be the ratings and peevish fury of callous men ?

What scheme the race may have devised before that date to relieve this cruel deadlock we cannot here discuss. The perfecting of the method of birth by Cesarean section offers much promise. It may become a racial necessity. This possibility, on which to-day we are beginning to impinge, indicates one great cause of the torturing agony of the actual hours of birth which the young mother and father-to-be may have to face before they can see the child of their love. A second cause of pain is the nature of the soft parts and of the womb itself. Its " neck " or opening is small throughout life, except at the times just before a birth when it has to relax enough for the infant's head to stretch it and pass through the strained muscles, and this sometimes causes great pain and even tearing of tissue. Then there are the contractions of the womb which are strong muscular movements calculated to expel the infant. These are technically called " pains " whether they cause a sensation of pain or are, as is rarely the case, rhythmic contractions which are without suffering.

Fortunate women are even still so constructed that the circle of bone has a relatively large orifice which allows the infant comparatively easily to pass through it, and the soft parts relax easily, hence the difficulty and danger of birth for them is minimized. With them the birth pangs may be so trivial in comparison with the result, that they are truly "almost negligible" as most men would like to believe of most women.

Such women, when outward circumstances allow it, are those whom every impulse should encourage to be the mothers of the large families, which are, under proper conditions, still desirable for a portion of our people.

Such a woman as the one who wrote me the following letter is indeed the standard which all women and would-be mothers would gladly reach were it possible in any degree to control the formation of a growing girl's body so that as a woman she might retain such a primitive adaptation to motherhood :

On the exact right day the babe arrived . . . in a quarter of an hour he was there, without nurse, doctor or any one and with no pain to myself. This little party has grown into a splendid specimen, very large (he was 8½ lbs. at birth) and firm and muscular. He is the whole day long laughing and kicking or sleeping.

Such women, however, so far as records go, are few. Much might be done by science to discover what are the causes of the reverse condition, and if possible to attempt to eliminate them.

In view of the agony which myriads of women throughout the ages of civilization have endured, it seems strange indeed that no effort should apparently have been made by the learned to understand the causes which control the individual formation of the growing structure, with a view possibly to securing some such development. In recent years, however, a little has been done in the recognition of the causes of the converse, that is to say the excessive narrowing of the pelvis to the degree where child birth is not only torment but a life and death agony. And it is now well known that this condition is associated with malnutrition and rickets in infancy and early girlhood.

The little baby girl who has rickety bones (which result from being improperly fed as an infant) is, in extreme cases certain, and in many cases very likely, to have such contracted pelvic bones that when her turn comes for motherhood, the birth of a living child may be impossible by the ordinary processes of Nature. Here again, as so often is inevitable, in the course of any considera-tion of the profound truths of mated existence, we impinge upon the treatment of the unsound and the diseased. This *under* development of the mother's pelvic bones is a different problem from that evolutionary one touched on in the paragraphs above.

Alas, that it should be true that the great majority of city dwellers come into the category of the spoilt and the tainted in some respect or another. But with the vision of true health and beauty as a standard before our eyes, many might escape the incipient weaknesses by consciously

pursuing a standard of health, beauty and normality.   It is this standard, this ideal picture,
which may yet be reproduced in the lives of
millions, which I desire to present in this book,
so that in telling young married people some of
the great facts which are ahead of them I will
present only those difficulties which are inevitable,
and leave to others the handling of disease.   As
things are to-day among British stock [1] it is the
very exceptional women who find birth an entirely
easy process of which the pain is trivial, and birth
stands as a gateway of pain between the infant and
the outer world, between the young wife and her
motherhood.

Before the hour of birth is reached, however,
the young mother-to-be, if she is neither instructed
nor helped by the wisdom of her elders, may have
already endured much that it will distress and
dismay her lover and husband to observe, and
much more which she, being a woman, will
endure without allowing him to perceive, although
she may be so frightened that it may be hard
indeed for her not to cry out in her bewildered
pain.   How much of this distress and pain is

[1] In this, and in most of the generalizations found in this
book, I am speaking of things as they are in Great Britain.
While to a considerable extent the same is true of America
and the Scandinavian countries, it must be remembered all
through that I am speaking of the British, and primarily of
our educated classes.

essentially " natural," how much is the artificial
result of our mode of living and our ignorance of
Nature's laws ?   What are the things which a
healthy, finely-built young woman mated to a
healthy young man must endure, those experiences which she *cannot* escape and those which
she may with proper help avoid altogether or
in part ?   It is the object of several chapters in this
book to answer these questions more truthfully
and I hope more helpfully than they have yet been
answered.   The things I deal with specially,
because they will face nearly every *healthy* girl,
are in most books ignored.

My chapters may appear superfluous to those
who view the long list of books purporting to
give advice to the young wife and expectant
mother on how to treat herself and the coming
child.   I have read the majority of those books,
and I write this one because of their failure to
touch on the profoundest essentials in a way
which will truly help the healthy and sensitive
type of young people.   The healthy, normal and
happy in my mind's vision are the standard of the
race : those who to-day to some extent foreshadow
the strength and beauty of bodily and mental
equipment which will become a commonplace
when all have risen to their standard, and it is for
them that I feel it imperative to add this one more
book to the long list of books advising the young
mother.   With the young mother I also consider

and try to help the young father who has been so strangely neglected and ignored and who also needs help.

The majority of the writers on cognate subjects, like the majority of the minds of those who are concerned at all with the problems of the young mother, really though perhaps unconsciously present studies in disease, pictures of aberrations from the normal, accounts or innuendoes dealing with illness and handicaps, with abnormal conditions which should never arise, and the knowledge of which should not be brought before the sensitive mind as if they were a usual and general thing. The acquiescence in a low standard of health, the discussion of diseased conditions as though they were normal, or even as though they were unavoidable, are intensive in their result and harmful to all who come under their influence. The race sickens ever more and more profoundly because of such influences.

We have to-day in our community a new conception in the Government Department of the Ministry of Health, but alas, that Ministry is engrossed in the contemplation of disease. In the present state of our civilization this is perhaps unavoidable, because there are not enough people in the country of standing and experience in scientific research who have concerned themselves with the problems of the healthy and beautiful, and with the needs and requirements in the way of instruction and outward conditions and environment of those who by nature are healthy and normal, and who desire to remain healthy and normal. Even these need instruction to compensate for that which Nature cannot give to those who toil apart from her bosom in the cities, where they cannot hear her voice for the roaring of the traffic. This is the piteous plight of the majority of our citizens to-day, for so many live in towns.

Alas, that there are physical facts which all must face of a type which makes one feel that Nature is cruel in her treatment of us. When two young, beautiful, and ardently happy beings are embarking upon the greatest work for the community which they can do, with a desire to create further beautiful and happy lives, it seems indeed an ironic and wanton mistake that there should be distressing physical experiences for both of them to endure. But " As gold is tried by the fire, so the heart is tried by pain," and if they are given a conscious knowledge of what they must face and what they may avoid, there will then be a firm foundation and a triumphant consummation to the visions and ideals of splendour and perfection which they can secure unimpaired through the trials which they conquer.

CHAPTER IV

The Young Mother-to-be :
Her Amazements

But lo ! what wedded souls now hand in hand
Together tread at last the immortal strand
  With eyes where burning memory lights love home ?
Lo ! how the little outcast hour has turned
And leaped to them and in their faces yearned—
  " I am your child : O parents, ye have come."

ROSSETTI : *The House of Life.*

THE intermingling of the physical, the mental and the spiritual is so subtle, intricate and inexplicable that, in describing the states of the bride who is about to be a mother, it is difficult to know with which first to deal.

In an Appendix, p. 229, I put in compact form one or two of the obvious physical phenomena with which it may be necessary for the bride and bridegroom to acquaint themselves. Although generally known to their elders, my many correspondents have shown me that even such simple and direct facts are often unknown to young people, who are frequently so shy that they do not like to consult a medical practitioner or an older friend. Assuming then that the simple physical facts are known, there still remain innumerable subtleties which may cause heart searching, perhaps to both bride and bridegroom.

It is almost as though the bearing of a child were a function so primitive in its origin that it tends, to some extent, to dissociate the ordinary coherence of the mother's life, and to result in a weakening of the sub-conscious control over her emotions to which she had all her life grown accustomed. Thus she enters upon a complex state in which primitive instincts and feelings may be at variance with the conscious thoughts and aspirations of highly civilized and sensitive humanity.

This complexity of her instincts and her conscious feelings may lead the young wife to find an apparently inexplicable conflict in her attitude towards her husband. Consciously she desires ardently, with all that is best in her nature, to bear the child of their love. She adores her husband and is full of tender emotions towards him as the coming father, and experiences a form of gratitude that he should be the means of fulfilling her dreams ; but possibly, at the same time, she may be amazed to

4

find in herself an intense and active antagonism to his personal presence, an antagonism which she has to fight against revealing. She may realize that it is utterly at variance with her real feelings, and she may know that it would be the acme of cruelty to allow him to become aware of it, particularly when he is full of deep concern and love for her, and is doing all that a loving consideration can do for her happiness and welfare.

Such a complex diversity of mental states existing perhaps co-incidently at the same hour in the mind of a girl may, if acute, lead to an outwardly recognizable form of hysteria and even to an unbalanced mind. Of such, however, I am not speaking, but am now describing the outwardly controllable, but nevertheless inwardly felt effervescing conflict of instinctive emotions, which is far more frequent than is generally recognized, and which the best balanced and most loving women are amazed to experience in themselves.

From women whom I know to be exceptionally happy wives and mothers, I have evidence on this theme. With, of course, personal variations, they tell me that they have never confided this bewildering experience to their husbands, their doctors or their relatives, but, in essence, they say what is said in the following words by one of my correspondents :—

In the first few months of coming motherhood she had a feeling of antagonism so strong
" that it amounted to actual dislike of my husband's presence, and a desire to be right away
from him. This distressed me very much at
first as I thought I must be losing my love for
my husband, and could not understand such a
sudden reversal of feeling as I loved him very
deeply. . . . At the end of the first three
months, I found that my feeling of love
returned in full strength, and with it a feeling
of intense devotion and tenderness towards
my husband as the father of my coming
child."

Some such experience, generally and fortunately limited to comparatively short though
different periods, is not infrequently felt and is
often a source of secret distress and anguish
to the young wife whose sense of loyalty to
the man she loves and married bars her from
the relief of talking of these feelings. As is
now beginning to be realized, emotions deeply
experienced which are deliberately suppressed,
may have far reaching effects even on the health.
It is, therefore, well that she should know what
is, I am sure, the truth, that this physical repugnance, which sometimes even amounts to a
detestation of sharing the same house with the
husband, and a desire to escape even from the
superficial contact of eating in the same room

with him, is a temporary phase, possibly phylo-
genetic [1] in its origin.

This passing phase, whether it lasts a few days
or months, is neither necessary nor absolutely
universal, but so far as I can ascertain it appears
to be a common occurrence in the lives of the
more sensitive and tenderly loving of wives.
Where the coming child has not been desired
by both parents, and where the mother resents
her coming maternity, there is, of course, a totally
different problem for which there is a very
obvious reason. I am speaking now only of
the mother-to-be who deeply desires her child,
who is physically healthy and well formed,
living under comfortable, protected and happy
conditions, and who ardently loves and is loved
by her husband ; it is she who may and most
frequently does feel this passing phase of intense
physical antagonism. That she loves, and consciously loves, gives her an outward control so
that this under-current of inherent antagonism
is not allowed to show, and is gallantly concealed
from the whole world. She would feel it an
intense disloyalty to speak of it to any living
soul, but it is there and it is so often a source

[1] That is to say, repeating the history of our very early
ancestors, where the female probably felt some resentment
towards the male who had encompassed her maternity, and
who most certainly would live apart from her and not in the
ordinary contact of a united life.

of distress and strain upon the nervous system that it should be openly faced instead of being as it now is a repressed feeling. This repression tends to result in one of the greatest difficulties of the *healthy* woman who is carrying a child, namely sleeplessness. The complex balance of her nervous control is strained by her surprise at herself, and perhaps by her self-reproaches, and thus she has an unnecessary burden in addition to the one of the coming child. This phase, therefore, is not a fact to be ignored or treated too lightly, and while it lasts it should be respected so far as is compatible with the circumstances of the two and with due regard for the mother. It is not a thing either to fear or to be ashamed of. It is perhaps best openly faced as a fact of rather curious interest as an ancient survival in oneself of racial history. If possible it should form the object of innocently playful laughter between the girl and her husband ; this would do much to prevent its suppression taking a serious root.

Aware of the existence of this phase and its probable meaning and treating it in this simple sensible way, neither the young mother nor the father-to-be need fear this brief physical antagonism. Where its danger lies, however, is in the possibility that unrecognized, it will, with those who live a shade less perfectly, result in the beginning of a habit of irritation, and perhaps in the setting up of some form of verbal bickering on the part of those who cannot lead as secluded and separate lives as would be possible in a spacious country or in a large establishment. When once the pair have broken the sweet custom of speaking only in love to each other, then, even after the temporary phase of antagonism has passed, they may find themselves with a habit of verbal bickering which is intensely corrosive, ultimately perhaps more than any other thing tending to destroy the outward beauty of a mutual life.

There is another and reverse aspect of the mental phases through which a young mother-to-be may pass, in which she has an intense and added passion for her husband, and, as this leads to a subject of great importance, and a subject which has never been adequately handled, I will defer its consideration to Chapter XII.

CHAPTER V

The Young Mother-to-be :
Her Delights

The sweet, soft freshness that blooms on baby's limbs—
does anybody know where it was hidden so long ? Yes,
when the mother was a young girl it lay pervading her
heart in tender and silent mystery of love—the sweet, soft
freshness that has bloomed on baby's limbs.

TAGORE : *Gitanjali.*

IN a happy and desired motherhood, every
hour of the day and night may bring
its intense delight, both in the dreams
of contemplation, wherein the experience of
love sinks deep into the heart, and of the linking
up of the present with the future. All natural
functions rightly performed give a deep satisfaction and content, but this, the greatest function
of all, now so specialized and intimately interwoven with every highest racial impulse and
every dearest personal desire of the loving pair,
yields a wealth and profundity of experience
surpassing all else.

In my opinion, undoubtedly the ideal way
of spending the earlier months of coming parenthood is in the form of an extended honeymoon,
in which the couple travelling slowly should
follow the guide of seasonal beauty or should
visit place after place of historic interest or
natural charm so that the mother's mind should
be fed and stimulated by historic memories,
by the exquisite freshness of nature, and the
grandeur of man's artistic achievements. This,
of course, would not be possible in its fullest
extent to many, until, in the future, society
recognizes the supreme importance to the race
of the expectant mother. Some such course,
however, might be possible to a larger number
than it is at present were they to realize not
only their personal good but the racial benefit
of this procedure. In our country, owing to
our artificial and unclean attitude, the mother-
to-be, particularly during the later months,
stays at home so far as possible, and does not
go from place to place. When going about
entails battling with crowds on public convey-
ances, this is wise. But the easy effort of walking or of riding in the old fashioned horse
carriage from place to place on an extended
journey, is ideal, and sometimes appears to
have beneficial reactions on the character and
quality of the child that is coming. But, even
if such a mode of life is impossible, yet the

mother by reading and conversation can, if she has a mind of trained imagination, vary and enrich the mental environment of her child while it is developing.

Then, too, the mother-to-be can count among her delights all the intimate personal enjoyment of the little physical things which contribute to the great anticipations of the future. She can, if she has the skill herself, sew the little clothes, stitching into them sunny thoughts and beautiful hopes, making them links between the present delightful *solitude à deux* and another beautiful time which the little one who is coming cannot comprehend till, many years hence, he or she will experience its charm in turn.

Little things intensely loved undoubtedly bring a greater reward in human happiness than great and numerous possessions, the joy of which can be but partly grasped. Within a tiny home, a mother whose heart vibrates with love can find a thousand sources wherewith to enrich the coming life.

But of all her delights, the greatest must always be the thought of the wonderful gift, which, at some ever nearing date, she will be able to give to the man whom she adores. Some men are negligent of the charms and enravishments of children, but I think in every man who fully loves and is fully loved by his wife, the thought of the child of them both must always be a stimulant to everything most ardently beautiful and profound in their natures.

Pictures of the child in after life filling brightly and beautifully some big position in the world may flit past the mother's mind during this time, but, if the mother is wise, she will not too intimately visualize the outward form of her child as a maturing girl or boy. By so doing she may indirectly wrong it. (See Chapter XIV).

Her delight should be to picture a tiny laughing messenger from God, thinly veiled so that its sex is hidden ; the figure of a child a few years old, still full of divine innocence and radiant possibilities. Happy hours of bodily rest may be spent picturing it in a thousand beautiful actions dancing in the sunlight, a contagious centre of joy in the whole world around them. On such an idea of delight she may lavish every day invigorating thoughts and wonderful dreams ; none will be wasted, of that she may be assured. If, at the same time, she is securing the coming child's bodily well-being through the proper material channels, then she can feel that these dreams of higher than material beauty are being built into reality. The secret sacred wonder of the process of which she is the active centre casts its spell of

magic and delight around the willing mother.
" A Garden enclosed is my Beloved," and she
feels within her own existence the mystic sense
of divine beauty, which one feels in another
form in a walled garden in the summer twilight.

CHAPTER VI

The Young Mother-to-be : Her Distresses

The amount of suffering that has been and is borne by women is utterly beyond imagination.

HERBERT SPENCER : *Principles of Ethics,* II.

THE bodily changes which at first almost imperceptibly steal upon the mother, if she be a girl who has enjoyed her own physical beauty, and has taken that care of herself which so delightful a thing as a young woman's body merits, will be at first a series of amazements and perhaps of delights as her body rounds itself and becomes more perfect. At this time the husband should fill his memory with her exquisiteness, for though she will, in the end, return perhaps to her normal strength and a re-awakened and different beauty, she will never again in her life reach such a point of bodily perfection as she does during the first three months or so of her coming motherhood, culminating at about the close of the third month.

As the years pass, hallowed and sanctified by love which is understood, even when grey with age, her face may gain an ever increasing beauty and power, but the perfection of her body is reached in the early days when she is first about to become a mother.

To one who cares for the outward form of her body, changes will occur inevitably as the months pass, which may give rise to deep distresses, principally because they feel at the time so permanent and it is difficult to believe that the disfigurements will ever pass. For a time she must inevitably become less and less beautiful ; she may indeed become, even to herself, repugnant. Perhaps to her as to so many thousands of women the sight of themselves then is a torment, and the conquest of this feeling is a great and increasingly difficult mental exercise. As this time approaches and is upon her, the young mother-to-be must concentrate all her conscious thought on the beauty of the future. She must forget the present and its cruel distortions and live in the months and years that are to come when she will have with her another life and lovely form to which she has given origin.

Nothing is at present gained for our civilization by the obstinate blindness on the part of some, and the wilful deception on the part of others, which together encourage the concealment from the bride of what she has to face.

On the one hand stand these prudes, but on the other the too eager and explicit, even lewd and profane and soiled minds who delight in lugubrious warnings.

The result has been that many a woman enters upon her motherhood gaily and eagerly, totally unprepared for what is to follow, totally unaware that, by the first act of motherhood, she gives up something essential to herself and something which is irreplacable in all the after years. So great a gift should be made not only voluntarily, but consciously, and with full knowledge of what it entails.

Cruel indeed is the callous hardness of the older mind that can see without desiring to help the proud and sensitive young spirit embarking upon a course which cannot but entail subtle difficulties at the best and extreme physical anguish at the worst, yet help of the kind the modern sensitive girl needs is almost unobtainable. Rare indeed is the mother of the last generation who has the power and the knowledge to meet the unvoiced demands of this.

Acquainted as I am with all sorts and conditions of men and women, I am nevertheless frequently amazed and filled with burning indignation at the well-nigh inhuman cruelty, stupidity and hypocrisy of the older generation towards young potential parents. It is not an uncommon thing to hear a man who is unfaithful to his wife because she has lost her physical beauty, at the same time haranguing the public on the compulsory duties of parenthood on the part of all young married women, and coupling his denunciations with sneers at the young girl who fears to embark on motherhood, reviling her as selfish. Yet the cause of her shrinking may be that from all the weltering confusion of contradictory and scrappy information which may have been allowed to reach her, the one which has fixed itself in her mind most vividly, is that which promised her loss of her bodily charm and that of all she possesses which is most valuable to her as a bond which binds her husband's affection to her. The woman who is perfectly sure of the continuance of her husband's spiritual and romantic love does not fear the risks of motherhood. All who truly and deeply love, desire parenthood. But can a woman who was married by a shallow man only for her beauty dare to risk the thing which holds him to her?

There is indeed a diabolical malignity in the older man who is himself unfaithful because of the very things in his wife which he denounces the younger girl for fearing.

This must not be misunderstood by my readers as indicating that I think a woman

should shrink in any way or that her husband
should grudge the sacrifice of all the fragrance
and beauty which they possess towards making
the child of their love the citizen of the future.
But with fervent intensity, I feel that to keep
the young woman ignorant of facts, and, at
the same time, on the one hand to upbraid and
bully her and on the other to terrorize her with
evil minded tales and tragic sights, is conduct
which would be laughable in its absurdity did
it not touch the spring of tears.

As the months of expectant motherhood
succeed one another the girl will find her power
to walk and run, to keep up with her husband
in his pleasure, his out-door exertions, or even
to do the usual standing involved in the course
of her house work, increasingly curtailed. This
is perhaps the inevitable consequence of the
burden of actual weight which results from
the later growth of the child within her as it
increases and approaches the size of a living
baby.

Sometimes the fortunate mother finds that
she is still capable of the same amount of exertion to which she is generally accustomed, but,
under modern conditions, this is but seldom.
The stories of Kaffir women on the trek who
bear their children and follow on with the rest,
and savages whose activity is in no way curtailed, are neither applicable to modern condi-

tions, nor are they fair standards to set, because such women do not live as the modern woman is forced to, nor is their bodily organization really comparable with that of our highly sensitive brain-evolved race.

Nevertheless, with the exception of heavy exertion, the girl who is carrying her child should be able to indulge in a much greater amount of healthful exercise, without undue fatigue, than she is generally able to enjoy. (See also Chapter X).

Most women have heard rumours of others who have been able to follow out almost all their usual occupations, and have felt little or no handicap from child bearing. Such an exceptional woman is my correspondent who wrote :—

I lived exactly as usual; I played golf up to the middle of the seventh month and bicycled up to my very last. On the afternoon of the day my second child was born (weighing 8¾ lb.) I was shopping with a woman acquaintance, who had no idea there was anything on the way.

Such women, although not very many, do exist among us. Their existence is perhaps the source of the hope which always animates every girl first embarking on her parenthood that she, by the sheer force of the longing for health which is within her, will prove also to be such an exception. Sometimes this desire may be apparently fulfilled, but generally, unless it is coupled with much greater knowledge than most girls possess, as the months pass one by one, her proud spirit will bend, she will give up and give up and give up. Humbled, weakened, humiliated before herself, through the fact that she is not strong enough to fight what she now is inclined acquiescently to call " Nature," she too goes down the stream with all the myriads of other happy hearted girls, whose gallant endeavours have equally failed. Then she creeps, wearily resting by the way, where she had hoped to tread with a firm and lightsome step.

There grows in her mind, and this is stronger the more she loves her husband, the added distress that she feels that she is failing him. He married a mate, an equal, who lighter of step could yet cover the ground as well as he, and who could share his amusements, his work to some extent perhaps, and his pleasures. She feels that she must, so far as she possibly can, maintain this position. This hope impels her particularly if they have been married but a short time, and hence their days of delightful untramelled companionship have been so few.

In this unselfish distress, which is primarily for him, she is tempted to conceal her effort and tends to overstrain herself in an endeavour to act as completely as she can the part, as reported, of the early Greek or Roman matron

or of the proud and savage mother who could
bear her children as lightly as a woodland creature.
Finding sooner or later that she *cannot* do so,
she suddenly gives in. Her strength, under-
mined by the series of distresses, the subtle
shocks and blows to which she is secretly subjected, she yields and takes on that air of semi-
invalidism, demanding constant care and consideration from her husband and those about
her, which in a way represents the hauling
down of her gallant flag. Her dreams of an
easy motherhood are vanquished.

She will at times be dimly conscious that
she is no longer able to feel so acutely. This,
in a way perhaps, is Nature's provision against
the too intense experiencing of emotion, which
would otherwise come with sensitive motherhood. The sensation can be described, as one
woman put it, as though each one of her powers
of feeling were wrapped round in cotton wool,
deadened and clogged so that they no longer
gave contact. This may be well, but it adds
in a dim way to the various distresses, a sense
of unreality and apartness, which, if it coincides
with that temporary antipathy to her husband,
which was noted on page 33, may make the
mother-to-be, for the time at any rate, indeed
a wanderer in the valley of the shadow.

CHAPTER VII

The Young Father-to-be : His Amazements

Till from some wonder of new woods and streams
He woke, and wondered more; for there she lay.
                                        D. G. Rossetti.

THE young father-to-be, though a real and very important person, has been curiously neglected by all and sundry who concern themselves with the affairs of the "expectant mother," "child welfare," and the other social and semi-eugenic matters about which well-meaning people have so voluminously written and so sedulously talked.

Sometimes jesting reference is made to the rather strange fact that, in some savage races, it is the father and not the mother who lies in bed for weeks after the birth of the child, but of the material and very real psychological experiences and physical difficulties which the young father is encountering and living through during the months before the advent of his first-born, few have any knowledge. Fewer still have offered the father-to-be any sympathy or help. Nevertheless with the increasingly perceptive and specialized individuals comprising our civilization, there arises an increasing number of young men capable of feeling and suffering in some degree corresponding to the great realities of which, for each, his home is the centre. And, moreover, it must not be forgotten that among our thoughtful classes are now growing up the young men whose mothers were among the pioneers of women's emancipation, whose mothers, therefore, were *voluntary* mothers who have trained their sons consciously and unconsciously, directly and indirectly, to be more in harmony with the true and natural attitude of a sensitive human being to its mate than are the average gross and over-bearing males, sons of enslaved and involuntary mothers. The sensitiveness of the modern young man towards his duties as a father, towards his wife as the mother of his child is, in my experience, very remarkable in its extent and its beauty. I have direct and indirect evidence from thousands that among the young Army men in various messes on the continent in recent years, an unexpected racial seriousness of attitude was shown when the necessary key that unlocked the secret chamber was available. Although it is a most deplorable truth, that there has been an increase in the racial diseases and an outward levity towards women, this is less an inherent baseness on the part of the young men than the result of the existence of the false conditions in which they have been placed, due to the criminal mishandling the whole racial problem has received from those older and in a position of authority.

In the nature of things, at first the young man can scarcely avoid taking fatherhood much more lightly than the girl takes motherhood. In normal, sweet, and healthy men, a desire for children of their own is very strong. Yet, however sympathetic their dispositions, however observant they may be of others, the unmarried young men cannot, under present conditions, have a full comprehension of what the attainment of motherhood involves in sacrifice for the mother. Hence the ideally mated young couple embarking upon parenthood set about it gaily, but before many months have passed, the young father-to-be must also be filled with amazements. For, control her impulse to be alone as she may (see Chapter III), curb her induced fretfulness as she may, the general psychological attraction between the man and the woman must be affected by the physiological state of the mother. The young man should find himself, if not actually repelled as the months progress, at least much more able to give his wife an impersonal tenderness in place of an active desire for physical union than he would have imagined possible. However sweet their love, if they are average human beings and not exceptional, he will perhaps, from time to time, be amazed and pained by unexpected peevishness and fretfulness, perhaps by what appear to be quite irrational and unjustifiable complaints from his wife. He should be made acquainted with the facts on page 43, and should apply them to himself and his wife. Knowing of the liability of such a temporary development, he can guard against any permanent injuries to love arising from the experience, such as often do result when it is unexpected and misunderstood.

I remember once being told by a nurse who had been at a large maternity home that of those who came there for the birth of their child she had only seen one couple between whom there was no bickering, not even infinite-simal criticisms and gusts of temper to ruffle the surface of their intense and romantic devotion. "Generally the women at this time," she said, "lead their husbands an awful dance, and are always snapping at them, but they do not really mean it, of course."

Men, on the whole, I think (although it is difficult and dangerous to generalize) are less tolerant of " superficial snappiness " than women, and the ruffling of the surface which comes with a few angry words enters probably deeper into the life of a sensitive man than it does in the life of a girl of corresponding type, although, on the other hand, a man may very quickly acclimatize himself to ignoring such comparative trivialities. Yet at first, at any rate, they not only amaze but distress, and when they appear irrational and swiftly pass, they may, although a trifle in themselves, be the cause of much misunderstanding and may be the foundation of more serious later disharmonies.

To the man who has any biological knowledge, all the wonderful processes of the growth of the unseen embryo, leading up to birth, are full of amazed wonder. If a man knows, as all should in these days (see my book, *Married Love*, for information about the fundamental processes of mating) how minute is the single sperm cell from which his growing child takes its rise, the immensity of the results of the activity of that tiny cell appear indeed stupendous. His flower-like bride is changed, her whole body is permeated, altered and impressed by the activities of this particle of himself united with its counterpart within her.

Only for the utterly callous can the experience of the months of waiting be anything but full of continual reminders of the amazing complexity of life. Long ago Tennyson felt :—

Flower in the crannied wall,
I pluck you out of the crannies,
    I hold you here, root and all, in my hand,
    Little flower—but *if* I could understand
What you are, root and all, and all in all,
I should know what God and man is.

Even more filled with humble and profound amazement must be the future father, who feels that his wife is now the very centre of the greatest mystery and wonder of the universe. Looking at her, brooding in her dreams, his mind must be continually filled with the consciousness of the eager active growth that is in progress, and the intense desire to take part in the mystical processes.

CHAPTER VIII

The Young Father-to-be :
His Delights

A Garden enclosed is my spouse, a spring shut up, a fountain sealed.

Song of Solomon.

IT is said that men naturally have a more casual interest in fatherhood than women have in motherhood. It is sometimes even definitely said that men do not have a passion for fatherhood or care profoundly for young children. This is not my experience. A much larger number of men than are credited with it feel an intense desire for fatherhood, and take a great delight in young children. Though they should share the joy equally, yet the father often has a larger proportion of the pleasure of the little child, while to the mother comes a larger proportion of the burden and the difficulties. To the child itself, too, the father is often more precious than the mother. An accidental testimony to this effect was given by the little daughter of one of those "devoted wives and mothers" who thought woman's place was only the home, and a mother's duty only to care for her children. The child and I were chatting and the little one misunderstood something I said, and thought that I asked which of its parents it loved most. The child quickly answered, "Oh, I like father best, *of course*—mother is there every day and she washes us." The privilege of being a child's favourite is no small one, and, as this child skows us, a father may win it with unfair facility.

The conscious dream of parenthood, a parenthood which shall give the children the best possible chance in life undoubtedly lies behind the majority of marriages. Hence when the young man who has married with the desire, perhaps not for immediate, but for ultimate fatherhood, first learns the definite fact that he has already inaugurated the beginnings of his child's development he must experience an intense and unique wave of feeling, which, as in the early days of marriage, with all its freshness, and with the actual physical difficulties yet unfaced, must be one primarily of buoyant delight.

There is also in the earlier months, for the man of artistic perceptions, an unique experience in the appreciation of his wife's enhanced beauty. It is perhaps known that the most critical artistic

view of woman claims the highest point of
perfection in her form about the third month
of her first period of motherhood. To a pair
of lovers who have delighted in their bodily
beauty, as all natural and healthy and well
formed young people should do, this period,
when the loveliness of the woman is at its very
height, and when the man can feel that he has
contributed to its perfection, must be a time
of very special entrancement. That it is something from within his most sacred being that
has added this glow and radiance in perfecting
the rounded form of the body that he adored
in its virginal grace, must give a man with
artistic and poetic potentialities an all too brief
but never to be forgotten experience. The
young father-to-be should not lose a day of
these swiftly passing weeks, for this phase, like
all human developments, but even more intensely
so than most, is passing and transient, only to
be immortalized in the permanence of a perceptive memory.

When, as is inevitable, it has passed, and is
followed within another month or two by a phase
so acutely, perhaps agonizingly its reverse, the
crucifixion of the mother's sensitive feelings
which is entailed should be hallowed and elevated
in both their minds by that deeper, less personal,
and more profoundly racial delight, the picturing
with each other of the radiance, the strength,

the power, the purpose and passion of the life which they are creating. So tragically soon after the days when he has feasted his eyes and filled his memory with her beauty, she will, she must withdraw her body from him and for months to come he will be shut out entirely from all sight of her. The reward will be an inner experience of the mind.

A day will come when, for the first time, the father-to-be may lay his hand upon his wife below her waist and feel the sturdy little kicks of his future son or daughter, and can know that, though hidden from him, still there is beside him a vital and independent being whom he has wakened to life. The presence of this little creature whom he has not seen colours and permeates every hour of their joint existence, and links the family in an extraordinary unity, the full significance of which I will consider in Chapter XII.

When the later months pass, the father-to-be will have lost one of his most exquisite memories if he has not already talked and laughed with his future child, and if he and his wife and child together have not united in that most mystical union possible to human flesh.

CHAPTER IX

The Young Father-to-be : His Distresses

When one knows thee, then alien there is none, then no door is shut. Oh, grant me my prayer that I may never lose the bliss of the touch of the one in the play of the many.

TAGORE : *Gitanjali.*

WITH all the passion for children, with the protective chivalrous feeling towards his wife which a well born and well knit man instinctively feels, through all the joy of fatherhood that is coming and the delight in its accomplishment, there must run a thread of intense distress at his own helplessness to help. With every consideration that the most resourceful man can think of towards his wife, with every helpful, tender, encouraging, supporting thing that he can do, how little is his share during all these months in the burden of the coming parenthood. If, through sympathy, he feels each pang his wife may feel ;

if, through sympathy, he curtails his activity to rest with her, nevertheless it is a voluntary abnegation, and if it became intolerable at any moment he could escape ; he could run over the hills ; he could go for a day's fierce solitude and activity wherever his feet desired to lead him ; but he knows that his wife *cannot*, that she is chained, that not for a moment of the day or night for nine months can she lay down the burden for a brief rest—that there is no exit for her from this imprisonment of so many of her potentialities but through the gateway of agonizing pain.

The instinct behind marriage is often a feeling of chivalrous devotion towards a tender and confiding girl, and the desire to give her every protection. The man finds, however, that his act has placed the one whom he desired to *protect* in such a position that she must bear the greatest burden possible for a human being to bear, and must bear it alone. This must be a deep distress to an imaginative man of integrity, although the distress be mingled with other and joyous feelings. To pretend that it is not so, to say that the joy of coming parenthood should and does wipe out all such undercurrents of thought is merely to be callous or silly. To repress an intense feeling, to pretend that it is not there, may give an apparent surface bravery or brightness. But such repression is ultimately destructive to the consciousness and whole physique of the one who, thus gallantly to himself, endeavours to deny the truth, and 's often apt to lead to deeper disorders. The modern school of psycho-analysts who endeavour to set right the effects of mental strain often discover that throughout life, perhaps dating from childhood, a personality has been handicapped and weakened by some deep suppression of an intensely experienced emotion.

In my opinion, the pretence that a sensitive man does not feel, and does not endeavour to conceal his feeling about his relation to his wife, particularly at the time of their first coming parenthood is to dishonour man's capacity and his imagination. Why imply that a rational man does not experience what surely all but a brute must feel. It impoverishes our life of emotional expression, and it tends to injure the man himself, to increase the strain by the pretence that the strain is not there. I know, for instance, one man who fainted at the time his wife gave birth to their child, and who, under no consideration, would allow her to have a second child, although he had intensely desired and looked forward to the fatherhood of a large family before he knew the actual physical experiences which it entailed. Such a man, in my opinion, was a good father wasted by an excess of emotion made all the more intensely des-

tructive to himself by the endeavour to maintain the totally artificial and indeed the crude
attitude which is supposed to be " correct " for
a man, namely a sort of dissociation of himself
from his wife's experiences and a hardened lack
of recognition of all that is involved. It is
surely better to recognize that there is that
intense and poignant sense of helplessness, that
the sensitive and developed young man should
and does feel it, but that it should be recognized
as the compensating price which he pays for
fatherhood.

If we are ever to raise our race to the point
when every child is so precious that no child
can be hungry, neglected or unwanted, the
conscious price which the *father* pays for his
children will be one of the assets in valuing
the children of the nation. It is, therefore,
better to acknowledge and encourage such sensitiveness in the father by allowing the open
and honourable expression of such feeling, and
thus to avoid that almost neurotic and destructive
effect of the suppression of such intense feeling
as warped the father mentioned above. Because,
if the wife avails herself of the advice I give
in this book, and if the time for parenthood is
chosen rightly and wisely in relation to her
general health, and it is ascertained before she
embarks upon potential motherhood that her
bodily and bony structure is fit for motherhood,

then though the experiences of both will be difficult and profound in their testing of the quality of each other, motherhood should not result in any excessive strain, and should indeed be a time of wonderful life activity.

With all needless ill-health, and wanton ugliness and wasteful distress which at present are artificially involved in it, once swept away, potential motherhood should not be an unendurable burden. Though the father's feelings should be intense and poignant on behalf of his wife and though she may go through searching experiences, yet the gladness should so preponderatingly weigh in the balance in excess of the troubles and difficulties that no normally healthy and well endowed young couple should ever suffer so much that they dare not face a second maternity, as happens alas only too often to-day.

On quite a lower plane, but nevertheless on the one so essential that it greatly affects all the rest of life, is the too frequent distress of the young father-to-be about the more material provision of all that is necessary for his wife. In counting the cost of the coming parenthood, too often quite heavy expenses are unforeseen, and, with a fixed income, the young man may have the intense distress of being unable to provide all that his wife not only wishes but really ought to have. Recent years, for instance,

were times of extraordinary difficulty for all
women who bore children, and who had a
naturally healthy and proper desire to eat fruit.
With oranges at a shilling each, as they were
in the winter of 1918–19, how could an ordinary
young couple afford a glassful of orange juice
a day, which I recommend as profoundly valuable (see p. 80). It was obviously impossible.
Such a time, of course, one hopes will never
be repeated. It was a period of undue strain,
when none, considering the future of the race,
should have borne a child unless private reasons
made it specially advisable.

But apart from such excessive and unpre-
cedented difficulties, there are, and probably
always will be, difficulties for the young man
who desires to provide everything that can
benefit his wife. Not long ago in the news-
papers, a budget of the cost of the baby in an
ordinary lower middle class home was given,
and there was an item : " Dentist's bill for
the mother, twenty pounds." A wise comment
was made on this that, alas, it is by no means
an unusual, indeed it is a usual experience that
the coming child adversely affects the mother's
teeth, and both for the health of the baby and
the mother they should be attended to. Possibly, even her very life may depend on her
teeth being thoroughly free from decay after
the birth. A heavy dentist's bill is too often

an unexpected anxiety to the young husband, so that the teeth are neglected. Neglected teeth either weaken, or may actually result in the death of the mother from their decay, causing internal poisoning, to which she is peculiarly liable after bearing a child.

Then too, there are unexpected and heavy expenses which are unforeseen through a variety of circumstances, such, for instance, as the uncertainty of the date of the birth. Those who go to nursing homes, as many are now doing owing to housing and service difficulties, experience this trial more acutely than others. They expect and plan, perhaps, for the birth within a given week, and the baby may delay two or three or even more weeks beyond the calculated time. Young couples, scarcely able to afford the heavy expenses of a good nursing home, who yet had saved sufficient to allow the wife three weeks there, may have their plans quite dislocated by a delay of three weeks in the infant's appearance, resulting in the mother unexpectedly having to remain double the length of time for which they had saved the money for the nursing home. The young father is then faced by the sordid difficulty of finding the necessary money, and unless he is gifted in such a way as to make extra earning a pos- sibility, is under a condition of strain. Just when all his free energy and time should be devoted to companionship with his wife and infant, he has to spend extra hours working at high pressure in order to meet unexpected expenses. The young father-to-be who wishes to maintain the right and beautiful atmosphere around his coming child should inform himself of all certain and likely contingencies of expense, and should make due provision for these before the great act of calling into being one for whom he is primarily responsible.

To a healthy man, also, there may be a period of chastening experience in sharing daily life with one who is out of health. Though the prospective mother *ought* not to be in any way invalided, yet, alas, as things are, too often she is, and only an unselfish man will fail to resent the personal sacrifice which he endures as a result.

There is a certain self-centred type of man who may, with the most model intentions and in order to lead a self-respecting life, marry, and who may find the resulting pregnancy of his wife very disconcerting to himself and very thwarting to his own requirements. With a certain bitter selfishness, this attitude was unconsciously expressed by one of my correspondents in the following words : " Something must be done to prevent any more children ; imagine what a wretched time I have with my wife sick every day for nine months." Perhaps the reader

can scarcely restrain a smile at so callously
self-centred an attitude on the part of a husband,
but, nevertheless, that man does have a real
and difficult physical problem before him. One
way, of course, in which to help such a man
would be to place such help and knowledge
before his wife that her motherhood should be
more normal, and not so terrible an experience
for her.

CHAPTER X

Physical Difficulties of the Expectant Mother

> We cannot reason with our cells, for they know so much more than we do that they cannot understand us; but though we cannot reason with them, we can find out what they have been most accustomed to, and what therefore they are most likely to expect; and we can see that they get this, as far as it is in our power to give it them, and may then generally leave the rest to them.
>
> SAMUEL BUTLER.

TO far too many women the time when they are carrying a child is a period of strain and semi-invalidism, a time filled not only with surprises and difficulties, but too often coloured with actual distress and ill-health. *This should not be.* The time of prospective motherhood should be one of buoyancy, health, physical activity and mental vitality. The low standard of health which the modern woman tolerates is deplorable.

But to whom can the young mother-to-be

turn for advice and assistance ? Such healthy, happy, prospective motherhood does not come by instinct in our city life. Those around her, older than she, who have had children of their own may perhaps be able to give her a hint here and a little piece of advice there, which to some extent may alleviate her difficulty or pierce with a faint shadow of light the gloom of perplexity in the ever deepening unknown into which she is entering for the first time ; but nearly all such women have themselves gone blindly and individually through this period of immense significance and mystery without having had any rational help from one devoted to the maintenance of *health*.

Almost every book written to advise the coming mother is written by a doctor of disease, with very few exceptions by doctors who tolerate what is, in my opinion, a disgracefully low standard of general health in women. A distinguished gynecologist who, in cross-examination before a commission persisted in maintaining that the " daily morning sickness " which is so prevalent in women who are carrying a child is " physiologically right and natural " (indeed, he implied almost that it was necessary) represents an attitude of mind very general and capable of far-reaching hypnotic injury to the community as a whole.

By far the best and sanest book available for

healthy women is one to which I have already referred, namely *Tokology*, by Dr. Alice Stockham, but this book has its inaccuracies and its drawbacks, and even its pages are too much occupied with the wretched and handicapping troubles which women do experience in large numbers, but *which should not be*.

Nevertheless, to allow a young girl or woman to enter upon these months of trial without making clear to her what she has to face, is cruel indeed. For a sensitive woman the experience, even at its best, and when most free from incapacities is, yet incredibly and penetratingly more terrible than she anticipated. The more sensitive and more conscious she is, the deeper and profounder may be her joy in her coming motherhood, but, at the same time, the more intense the physical experiences through which she must pass.

The modern sensitive young woman does not take things blindly and patiently and with resignation, with a pious belief in her own inferiority, which may have helped to dull and moderate the sensations of her grandmothers. The more evolved she is, the more she may be willing to bow to natural law, but the less is she content to suffer wanton cruelties imposed upon her by ignorance, stupidity or coercion.

Many are the midwives, maternity nurses and medical practitioners with whom I have discussed such matters, and from whom, often incognito, I have asked advice. I may say that *none* gave *all* the *necessary* advice, not one gave one-tenth of what is in this book, only one or two gave any necessary simple advice in the sympathetic and understanding fashion desirable, and only one or two appeared to have any clear *generalizations* or scientific understanding of the facts about which I asked. The resignation, the shrugging of the shoulders in the face of things which would otherwise make one weep, or the cheerful braving out or pretending that things are not as bad as they are, which is the general attitude of mind of the maternity nurse is little more helpful than that of the practitioner. Concerning many of the practical facts of the later months of pregnancy and actual birth, and the succeeding weeks of recovery, the properly trained midwife seems on the whole wiser than the average general practitioner, wiser even than the specialist who may come at a crisis, but who does not watch his patient through the succeeding weeks.

Many young women who have recently been mothers have told me of the mental and physical horror which they then experienced, and of the added horror that they should feel horror. They have asked me to generalize, if it is possible, from their cases in such a way as to help others who enter upon maternity's difficulties for the first time, so that they may at least be spared that terrible sense of isolation and of exceptional failure when they experience one by one the things which are inevitable, or the things which are, by our artificial lives, so frequently imposed.

The bearing of a child very often may be complicated by actual disease, and then requires, of course, expert medical attention. With those who are in any sense actually ill, and who should be in the hands of a doctor, I am not here dealing, for, in this respect, as throughout my other books, I desire only to write of health for the healthy so that they may have sufficient knowledge to maintain their health and raise the vitality of the race.

I may say here that, even for the healthiest, it is very advisable, not only for her first, but for every succeeding pregnancy, that a woman should be examined and measured by some wise and healthy-minded medical practitioner or midwife at least once during the first three months and twice again during the last three months, but that, for the first baby, it would be better to go at least every month for examination. In that way, the various insidious disturbances of the excretory system, and other fundamental things which *may* go a little wrong, even in an otherwise healthy woman, can be detected immediately and dealt with. Many however, find a great difficulty in bringing themselves to do this.

Undoubtedly it is much better for the prospective mother to go to a specialist, old enough to be wise and experienced and mellow, and yet young and virile and active enough to be acquainted with modern knowledge, and healthy and clean enough to look for and to desire health and normality in those who come for advice.

This should pre-eminently be the special field for women doctors, but there is not nearly a sufficient body of them with the necessary qualifications to meet the requirements of the community, and I should like to see a new profession created for women who, to the experience and the training of first-class midwives, have added a sufficient training in general medicine to be specialized to advise the *healthy* prospective mother, and to be able to detect at once anything which should necessitate handing her on to the doctor of disease. Such practitioners should rank in status somewhere between the cultivated midwife of gentle birth (such as a Queen Charlotte's Hospital nurse) and the medical woman. Thus the prospective mother would be spared that hard and bitter contact with one who has become myopic in the observation of disease, and would be able to go to someone specially trained to encourage health. Meanwhile, as this is but a bright picture of

what may come in the future (and that *will*
come if women make a sufficient demand for
it) it may spare many women distress if I set
out the physical difficulties and peculiarities
which are most liable to occur with a *healthy*
woman.

From the welter of accounts of the effects of
pregnancy, I have disentangled into three groups
those which normal women may have to face.
The difficulties are :—

(1) Those nature-imposed ; these are essential ; they cannot be avoided by the healthiest
woman. They can be perhaps, to some extent,
mitigated. They are things which the coming
mother must be helped through and over ; she
cannot be saved from them.

(2) Those entirely artificial ; these are quite
needless and are the results of either ignorance
or our gross disregard of known facts, and can
be entirely eradicated.

(3) Those which are to-day very usual, but
which knowledge and a better mode of life may
entirely conquer.

Now to consider first the third group : those
which are general, but which a knowledge could
or should conquer.

One of the first signs that she is to become
a mother, and one of the most usual experiences
of a young woman when this time begins, is
the daily recurrence of that penetrating nausea

and sickness usually after she has risen in the morning, called " Morning Sickness." This is so usual that medical practitioners rely on it to some extent as a sign of pregnancy. It is described in almost every book for the prospective mother, and, as I have mentioned (p. 72), it is sometimes even maintained by distinguished gynecologists as a physiological function, *i.e.*, a normal function.

Now this is a very nauseating and wretched experience to the majority of women, and it is one which, I maintain, is entirely imposed by ignorance, wrong living and the general hypnotic effect of others' perverted views on the woman's system. In those women whose internal organs are improperly placed or somewhat malformed, it occurs as a physiological result of pressure or other disturbance. *In true health there is no physiological reason whatever for the morning sickness*, and a woman who lives as she should live during the time of her coming motherhood need not experience it. This should, in the next generation, be entirely conquered, because it is to a very large extent caused by allowing, even forcing to wear corsets, girls when they are still unformed and developing. Those women who have never worn corsets in the whole of their lives, and who dress as they should dress, and do as they should do during the months when they are becoming mothers, seldom experience morning sickness. Though there are some who, when they know the child is coming, discard their corsets too late, and these may still experience this unpleasant feature. The extraordinary adaptability and vitality in a woman's system, however, is a remarkable thing, and even those who begin later in life than they should to train for motherhood may yet accomplish much.

Granted a healthy, well-formed body, a previous life of normal activity, sensible attention to the following points will insure complete freedom from morning sickness in all but the exceptional and pre-disposed :—

(*a*) Discard every scrap of heavy or constricting clothing, wearing only the lightest garments hung from the shoulders entirely. Discard also high-heeled and pointed shoes, wearing comfortable low-heeled boots and slippers.

As I said in *Married Love* the standard of dressing for the prospective mother, whose garments should be of the lightest wool and silk if possible, and should be so lightly hung that a butterfly can walk the length of her body without tearing its wings.

(*b*) Discard all rich, heavy and over-cooked foods, such as pastries and hot cakes, dried peas and beans, rich game or highly seasoned dishes, and live as much as possible on uncooked foods and simple milk puddings, stewed fruit, lightly cooked meat and fish, with the largest obtainable quantity of very fresh ripe fruit.

(*c*) Start the day not with tea, but with the juice of two or three oranges squeezed into a tumbler.

If she does these things a normal woman may go through the whole nine months without experiencing one single moment of nausea, as many a woman has done.

A retardation of the action of the bowels or constipation is very frequent, and is a cause of many other ill-effects. A right diet such as I advise, adding for this purpose honey and brown bread, does much to prevent it ; if it exists in spite of this, take suitable bending exercises (see also page 72), even a warm hydrostatic douche (using a douche-can with a little common salt in the water), but do *not* take regular drugs or " aperients."

Another of the very frequent experiences of the mother who is carrying a child, particularly towards the later months, is the enlargement of the veins of the legs and ankles and the formation of varicose veins. These may become very serious if neglected, and even if the woman is being doctored, unless, at the same time, she regularly follows the proper healthy method of dieting and living. In addition to the dieting and clothing described above, which will make her almost certain to be immune from varicose veins, she should take warm comfortable sitz baths every evening, and she should lie down for at least half an hour or an hour in the middle of the day or early evening with her feet raised a few inches above the level of her head.

One of the most serious difficulties, felt even by those who avoid all other drawbacks, is sleeplessness, particularly in the last month or two when the activities of the child may be very disturbing. In this, much depends on the position in which the child is lying, and sometimes the position of the child can be improved by massage and manipulation by a trained midwife or doctor. Something also can be done by the mother herself through her mental attitude and hand touch on the child, and also by taking hot sitz baths nightly before going to bed. Still more, however, is accomplished by right diet, clothes, exercise and happiness (see also Chapter XII).

The habit of taking aspirin regularly or in large quantities, which too many women indulge in if sleepless during this time, is extremely bad both for the child and for the mother. Drugs of any sort should not be appealed to. If it is possible during these later months, sleep will be much more refreshing, and the advantage will be very great both to the coming child and the mother, if her bed can be arranged on a verandah or out of doors, but it must not be forgotten that towards the end of the period

the expectant mother ought not to be out of
ear-shot of someone.

Now to consider the second group of dis-
abilities ; those entirely the result of artificial
outlook and condition. Among these must be
classed the inability to walk any distance or to
take part in active work of any sort. This is
partly imposed by the hesitation of a woman
to be seen at this time, and particularly to face
the vulgar and leering attitude of the general
public, and it is partly also due to the general
heaviness or strain on the muscles or to the
presence of varicose veins. If these have, by
the methods just described, been almost or
entirely avoided, she will find that her natural
activity is much less reduced than it would
otherwise be. To walk a mile or two, or even
three miles the day before or even the day of
the birth is not at all beyond what can be expected
from an ordinary healthy woman who lives as
she should.

The necessity perpetually to be fussing, to
be taking tonics or drugs or medicines, to be
thinking only of herself and never of any general
or greater theme, is also eliminated when the
general health is improved, and any mental or
bodily activity which the mother can indulge in
without a sense of strain is advantageous to
the child as well as to herself.

The highly nervous condition and overstrained

state of so many modern women during this time is due entirely to the artificial social lives, involving late hours, which they try to lead. The mother-to-be should give up almost all social engagements which keep her out of bed after 9 o'clock. Sleep, fresh air, exercise under the healthiest natural conditions she can command, coupled with the right diet, will secure her health and strength throughout the time.

The difficulties, however, about which help is most needed are the first group, those nature-imposed and inevitable difficulties which the woman *has* to face, and which, without instruction in the things she might do to mitigate them, often lead her to suffer intensely, though needlessly, and tend to have life-long effects on her health and appearance. Simple and sometimes obvious precautions are required, and yet these are almost unknown to the generality of advisers to whom the prospective mother can turn.

The first and most obvious inmost change that affects her is that felt in the muscles below the waist, particularly those which run vertically, and which support, by their elasticity and strength, the whole front of the body. As the months pass and the child and its attendant tissues grow, there is a slowly increasing strain on these muscles. As the enlargement proceeds the skin will also stretch, and the under-skin and tissues beneath it are finally stretched almost to breaking-point, stretched sometimes so that they do break apart and leave ultimate permanent little scars under the skin of the mother. Few apparently know, but all *should* know, that this can be almost entirely avoided (by fortunate women entirely avoided), if the skin and tissues immediately below it are kept supple by daily rubbing with olive oil from the fifth month. Perhaps from the fourth month once a week, and certainly from the fifth month daily, the mother should rub the lower part of her body and her breasts with a little olive oil. This will not only have a soothing effect upon the skin, but will assist its elasticity in such a way that she may return to her virgin condition without leaving those tell-tale scars which so often mark a woman, and which many, even highly trained maternity nurses and doctors, seem to think are inevitable. Such scars *are not inevitable*, and this very simple precaution, coupled with exercise, will frequently be sufficient safeguard for the woman who desires to avoid them altogether.

The same internal growth which enlarges the muscles and strains the skin will also sometimes press apart the two main vertical muscles in such a way that there is a tendency for inner tissues to project, and for the last month or two this may be very uncomfortable without

In any way being dangerous. It is then advisable to wear a small stiff pad over this and fasten it in place with a narrow, soft elastic band. The use of a localized plaster very often strains the skin and leaves scars or makes it sore. It is wise to have the small hard central bandage wherever there is a tendency to localized projection as will be self-evident to anyone who experiences it.

The natural darkening of the colour of the skin when it is strained and stretched as it must be is very displeasing to the eye and, particularly to a young girl whose beautiful body has been her delight, may be a cause of great distress and self-repugnance. It is well that she should be helped over this most anxious time of self-detestation by the reliable assurance that it is only a temporary phase, and that if she keeps in good health, and rubs herself with pure oil for two or three months after birth as well as before, the skin will be entirely freed from any stained or discoloured appearance, and will return to its normal condition.

As the months pass, the actual physical weight of the body will increase, gradually becoming a greater burden, so that long distance walking and any acute activity such as running or tennis-playing must become impossible. Nevertheless if the diet and mode of living suggested above is followed out this will be very much less embarrassing than is usually experienced.

Many forms of support or maternity corsets are advertised or medically recommended to assist supporting the weight at such times, but, unless the woman has any actual slipping of the position of the organs or any deformity, she is very much better not to take such proffered assistance for they will form a broken reed, and, as one knows, " the broken reed pierces the hand." It is much better for her to strengthen her own muscles by slow and careful exercise, bending forward until she touches the ground or as nearly touches the ground as possible ; also lying on her back on the ground and rising without touching the floor with her hands and arms ; also slowly raising the feet forward above the head while lying on the back, and then allowing them to drop slowly to the ground, this last exercise being very strengthening to the central muscles of the body wall (detailed accounts of other useful exercises will be found in Dr. Alice Stockham's *Tokology*). So long as there is no strain upon her, she should exercise throughout the whole of the time. She would then not need any artificial support, and would be much better without it.

I have never seen it elsewhere clearly stated, but I have discovered that one very important reason against corsets is that, however well shaped and loose they may be, they tend to touch and exert some slight pressure on the soft tissues at the back of the waist ; they must do so, merely to remain upon the body without dropping off, and this amount of pressure is sufficient to induce morning sickness (see p. 88) for the following among other reasons. As the womb grows in the centre of the body it pushes aside and to the back the many yards of soft tubular alimentary canal which normally lie coiled in the front of the body, and, if there is no constriction or pressure, these tend to find room for themselves round the waist line and to the back, so that there appears what seems almost like a coil or roll of fat round the waist. This disposition is very advantageous, however, and should not be interfered with in the way any corset must interfere, and it greatly reduces the ungainly frontal size and helps to keep the body better balanced (see p. 91).

At first the breasts will become firmer and larger and will support themselves more readily than at any time, but later on their shape somewhat changes and they tend to fall. They should then have carefully slung and properly arranged supports looped over the shoulder. Neglect of this often results in the final and lifelong loss of the beauty of the bosom, and it is indeed a cruel thing that the average doctor or nurse appears not to be capable of giving any useful advice on this point, so that hundreds of thousands of women have not only lost their beauty, but have been told that it is an inevitable and natural result of having borne a child. That it is well-nigh inevitable under modern unaided conditions, may be true. With proper support, proper massage and treatment afterwards, the ugly breasts need not have been, and need not be.

A thing which often distresses girls, but which however unsightly it is while present is a temporary and passing phenomenon, is the sudden appearance of freckles, even large patches of brown colouring matter, on the skin during the time the baby is forming. So far as I am aware nothing can be done to prevent it, and if as sometimes happens these brown patches even appear on the face, it is a misfortune which must be endured as stoically as possible, encouraged with the knowledge that it will entirely pass.

Another curious thing I know one woman experienced, and about which I am awaiting further evidence, was the apparent transplantation by the child in the mother of the strong black body hairs of the father. The result was that during the later months of carrying and for a few months after birth, the mother's lower limbs and forearms had a thick growth of

masculine-like hair, which nearly all fell off
within six months after the birth.

The tendency that the coming child has to
extract nutriment from the mother's tissues
often results in the loss or temporary spoiling
of two of her beauties, the beauty of her nails
and the beauty of her hair. These are apt to
suffer unless she is warned in time and protects
them. The injury to them probably depends on
the withdrawal of the proper quantity of fat
from the tissues. It is, therefore, advisable for
the mother-to-be to rub her nails and hair with
some suitable natural oil. Refined paraffin,
almond oil or castor oil for the hair are by far
the best, and for the nails some animal grease
such as lanoline, or perhaps simple vaseline.
Expensive concoctions, very much advertised
and claiming wonderful properties, generally
owe anything which they may contain to these
ingredients, but more frequently contain little
or nothing of any value, and are often harmful.

The more fundamental, and, alas, almost
inevitable result of bearing a child is that it
extracts not only the fat from the system, but
the hardening matter from the teeth. This
indeed is, so far as I am aware, a theft from
the mother by the next generation which no
knowledge of its liability can prevent, and
which can only be met by a careful supervision
of the mother's teeth both before and after

birth. Women differ in the amount they lose, but it is, alas, one of the almost inevitable things that there shall be a certain weakening of the teeth. Sometimes this will right itself and teeth which shook in their sockets immediately after the birth may apparently harden again and refix themselves firmly, but if the weakening takes the form of actual decay, they must be attended to.

In this respect the diet recommended by Dr. Stockham in *Tokology*, which advocates the elimination of all calcareous food is perhaps inadvisable if strictly followed out, because the growing child insists on mineral matter, and it simply takes it from the mother's structure if it does not get it in other ways. I have, therefore, thought it advisable not entirely to eliminate the wheat and other bone making materials from the usual diet as Dr. Stockham recommends, but to maintain a certain proportion of wheat, especially whole wheat, in the food. Her advice to replace rich dishes by simple rice, stewed fruits, etc., is certainly wise, and still more important is it to follow her warm recommendation to eat large quantities of fresh fruit.

One of the perfectly natural, but to the young mother rather unexpected, results of the changes of the later months is the alteration which gradually comes in the position of the centre of gravity of her whole body. She is of course scarcely conscious of this, and yet it is a point of some importance, because it results in a certain liability to slip and to fall, particularly coming downstairs. The danger of such a fall is less to the child, which is safely surrounded by a buffer of fluid and by the mother's protective muscles, but more to the mother herself, who, in falling, may strain or injure herself. The growth which results in this change in the centre of gravity comes too rapidly for the system quite perfectly to adjust itself to it. It will be remembered how long it takes a baby to learn to balance itself upright upon its feet ; the adult mother-to-be has had a whole lifetime knowing just how to balance, and every muscle has become adjusted to the centre of gravity in its accustomed place. The change in the distribution of weight changes the position of the centre of gravity to some extent, sufficiently at any rate to throw the co-ordination of many years somewhat out of gear, and it is, therefore, wise for the expectant mother to take particular care not to slip or stumble unexpectedly. The sudden and active movement of the child which may kick or turn with no warning may cause her quite to lose her balance, particularly if she is on a steep staircase. It is well, therefore, to make a special point of keeping guard against this possibility by always having a firm grip on the handrail when going up or down stairs during the later months of carrying a child.

However well and full of a sense of power and creative vitality she may be, a woman should take long hours of rest : to bed at nine each evening and not up till eight o'clock in the morning and taking at least one hour lying down during the day. During the nine months of bearing the unborn child, she should remember she is providing it with *vitality* every second of the twenty-four hours of each day, and she should neither have forced upon her, nor should she desire to do, work which ever tires her, though she should live an active, full, healthy, happy existence and should be capable of nearly all her normal work and enjoyments. If she is wise she will work in direct contact with sun-lit earth. Gardening ensures the truest sense of physical well-being.

CHAPTER XI

Physical Difficulties of the Expectant Father

I was a child beneath her touch,—a man
When breast to breast we clung, even I and she,—
A spirit when her spirit looked through me,—
A god when all our life-breath met to fan
Our life-blood, till love's emulous ardours ran,
Fire within fire, desire in deity.

D. G. ROSSETTI.

THE higher the evolution of the creatures, the more is the parental responsibility shared by both parents. Among human beings the institution of monogamy, which is universally accepted as a higher form of human relation than polygamy, involves in the dual partnership a certain sharing of the actual physical difficulties of parenthood by the father which is not entailed in the fatherhood of a polygamous establishment. In fact, a pure monogamy strictly maintained, does really affect the physical aspects of expectant fatherhood *more* than it

does the physical aspects of expectant motherhood.

The modern pair, being intensely and deeply
united, the effects of the experiences and physical
states of one have actual reverberations and
physical effects on the other.   In this respect the
change in the girl's attitude of mind towards the
man, which is sometimes a result of the physical
effect of motherhood (see Chapter III), may have
a very far reaching influence upon the man's
health and happiness if he does not comprehend
the cause of this experience, and, through comprehension, know how to endure or overcome
it.   Undoubtedly a home which is disturbed
by uncomprehended antagonisms or suppressed
irritations has a physical effect on the general
mental balance, and consequently on the whole
health of the pair involved.

The way in which these difficulties can be
overcome is by a mutual comprehension, so
far as is possible, of the needs of each other, and
sometimes perhaps by the attitude of " bowing
before the storm " until it has passed, recognizing
that it is a phenomenon beyond human control.

Beyond this may be subtler and more intricate reverberations from his wife's state.
The actual physical fact has to be faced by the
father-to-be that perhaps rapidly following on
the period when all his natural desires for a
completed sex union with his wife were met

and consummated by equal desires in her, there comes a time when such impulses on his part are not only not responded to by his wife, but are perhaps antagonized and may be entirely thwarted by either her mental or her physical condition.

In Chapter XII, I will show how, to some extent, and at probably rather long intervals, his impulses may be not only satisfied but may be harmoniously responded to and may be profoundly valuable. Nevertheless, in almost every period of coming fatherhood, there will be at least some months when bodily union is actively repugnant and consequently actively harmful, to the wife. At such a time the instinctive feeling of the mother against any act should be sufficient to bar it, because, even if the act itself should not be harmful, to force her will at such a time or to lure her into coercing herself against her own will is in itself harmful. A young husband, therefore, will be faced by periods in which it will be impossible for him to have any of the unions to which he may have become accustomed and which his natural virility may at first continue to demand.

This difficulty is of very varying intensity for different types of men. Some feel it so acutely that, although they may do so with deep shame, they yield to the impulses and are unfaithful to their wives in a bodily sense just at

the time when of all others they may be mentally
and spiritually most deeply united to her. Such
shameful conflict of will with deed must have
blackened many a father's memory, and, with
due understanding of all the circumstances, it
should be eliminated from our race : it should
not take place. Nature has created a way out
for the man who deeply loves and is in sympathetic rapport with his wife. While the wife
on whom he centres all his desires and love
is in a bodily condition which deprives her
from such an experience as a complete union
with him, this fact has a mental and consequently
a physical reaction on the better type of man,
and he finds, sometimes even to his surprise,
that the instinctive impulses to which he has
been accustomed die down. At first perhaps
becoming only sufficiently dormant to be conquered by a deliberate exertion of the will,
but as the weeks pass and the inhibition from
his wife increases, its reaction stills his desire
also, and his need for unions may temporarily
cease.

This is partly to be explained as a nervous
reaction due to his anxiety and his concentration
of nervous force on his wife, which tend to
inhibit the setting free of the vital energy which
would otherwise demand an outlet.

The vitality, the physical state, the needs,
however, of different men vary very greatly,

and there are those who really do require some
physical assistance in addition to will power
and even a religious determination to help them
through this time of difficulty. For such I
recommend daily thorough washing in cold
water of the organs of generation, and when
an over-mastering desire may come, the soaking
of the whole body in as hot a full length bath
as can be borne.

It may perhaps sound fantastic because one
has not yet scientific proof (neither had Leonardo
da Vinci when he casually made the first announce-
ment that our earth is a planet of the Sun),
but I think, in addition to the physical presence
of the secretions potentially demanding exit,
that a very important factor in the desire for
sex union is an electrical accumulation within
the system, and undoubtedly the soaking in
hot water tends to disperse this tension, and to
allay the urgency for a desire for a sex union.

These two simple physical assistances, com-
bined with a definite will to maintain himself
purely for his wife, and the definite concentration of his nervous energy to her support with
the desire to contribute everything possible,
mental and bodily, to the well-being of his
child, should suffice to keep the body of a normal
man in that condition which his best instincts
will approve. Others more acutely handicapped
by incorrigible physical requirements, may

have a hard time ; if it is insupportable, the explanation of that may be the existence of some slight physical abnormality for which they should and can get medical treatment.

After the restraint of the time of betrothal, followed by the usage of the honeymoon, the strain of almost total deprivation again, due to the wife's pregnancy, is greater on the husband than it need be ; and this is another argument in favour of deferring conception for at least some months or a year after the wedding. (*Cf. Married Love*, Chapter IX).

Even when, as is indicated later, there may come times when the impulse of the potential family is to unite, the physical condition of the mother may offer a hindrance to the customary form of union, but this with tact and intelligence may be surmounted.

CHAPTER XII

The Union of Three

" The Kingdom of Heaven is within you."

IN the early days of our modern civilization, that is to say within the last couple of hundred years, the treatment of women in Western Europe sank to a terribly low ebb. Although the last few years have done much to restore woman to some of her ancient rights and privileges, there are still among us a distressing proportion of ignorant, coarse and consequently ruthless men who are not debarred from becoming husbands. Such men have been in the past in the habit of " using their wives " regardless of the desires or even the actual health requirements of the unfortunate women who are tied to them, and such men have made a practice of continuing to indulge in sex union even through the later stages of pregnancy. I have heard from midwives, to my amazed horror, that some such depraved men (not bestial, for no beast behaves in such a way) have even used their wives while they are still in bed after child birth. With such I have in this volume no concern beyond the mention that they are loathsome.

Their existence, however, has had an effect on a better type and has given rise to reaction on the part of men infinitely their superiors. Women who have seen their sister women thus outraged have had the support of men of sensitive conscience and consideration when they have claimed that the mother who is carrying and nursing her child is sacred, and must not be approached by her husband at all during the whole of the child's coming and nursing period. It has, therefore, come about that a large number of our best and most high-minded women (supported by correspondingly high-minded men, anxious to do the best that is within their power for their wives and children) hold the view that no sex union after the third month, or perhaps that no sex union at all is allowable during pregnancy.

Now this is one more matter which has not begun to receive the consideration which it deserves. When I wrote *Married Love* I felt that I was not entitled to decide on this subject, and I tried to hold the balance between the various opinions, and drew attention to the fact that the prospective mother of the lower creatures is always set apart. This was apparently misinterpreted by some of my readers as being a personal expression of opinion, and women wrote or spoke to me about the subject saying they were sure I was right *because their husbands held the same opinion as I did*, BUT *the women themselves were ashamed, almost humiliated, to confess that during the carrying of their child they most ardently desired unions.*

To these, as individuals, I pointed out that I was very far from expressing a definite opinion in my book on this point, and that my actual opinion indeed inclined towards thinking that restricted unions should be advantageous. In a later edition (the 7th) of my book, I enlarged on what I had to say on this subject, concluding : " There is little doubt that in this particular, even more than in so many others, the health, needs, and mental condition of women who are bearing children vary profoundly."

Through evidences from very various types of women in the last year or two, I have now accumulated facts in sufficient numbers to begin to see something approaching a possible generalization on this subject.

One of the most striking things I noticed concerning the evidences I received was that the women who confessed to a desire for sex union while they were carrying a child were, almost without exception, the *best* type. A hasty generalization would have predicted that

those very women with their pure attitude,
their high degree of culture, their intellectual
attainments, and their gracious self-restraint in
outer life were just exactly those women who
would maintain a fierce chastity during the nine
months. These quite remarkable corresponding
experiences of similarly superior women forced
the matter vividly upon my attention, and I
am now prepared to make a tentative generalization, coupled with the generalization to be found
in Chapter XV.

The attitude of one of the women who confessed her intimate feelings to me is typical of
those of this type, and is illuminating. She is
a woman of unusually gifted brain, well endowed
physically and a normally healthy mother in
every respect ; she is noted for a peculiar beauty
and sweetness of disposition, and an unusually
high degree of sensitive appreciation of beauty
and goodness. In conversation she said to
me : " You know I feel so ashamed and degraded
by myself, but just at the time when I felt I
ought to be sacred from these things, I more
ardently desired my husband than I had done
throughout all my married life of fifteen years."
She then told me that her husband who had
been truly devoted to her all his life was particularly considerate and thoughtful for her
during her time of expectant motherhood, and
that when she tentatively hinted at her wish

for union with him he refused tenderly on the grounds that the higher standard for men was to share, however difficult it was, in the nine months of complete abstinence. He said that, for the sake of the child and herself, he must refuse. Her desire, however, again recurred, much to her own shame and mortification, because she felt that what her husband said really represented the highest accepted standard of pre-natal conduct. Quite a number of rather similar and also exceptionally endowed women have confessed to me in almost the same terms the same feeling.

Before I indicate my conclusions, let us briefly consider some of the surrounding circumstances of this problem. As I said in the opening paragraphs of this chapter, the nobler and better men have been carried away by a certain type of woman into thinking that it is man's share of the difficulties and self-sacrifice of parenthood that he should entirely sacrifice what is spoken of as " his desires." In my opinion, this attitude involves two profound fallacies. The first fallacy is that the act of sex union is to meet only " his desires ", it is not. Completed union is something infinitely greater : it is a consummation jointly achieved by both the man and his wife. This attitude I make clear in my book, *Married Love* and in my new *Gospel* addressed to the Bishops at

Lambeth. And I must postulate in this, my present book, the far reaching effects on the bodily, spiritual and mental health of a man and woman concerned in this complex sex union. The truth is that the husband who mutually and considerately unites with his wife when she can accept him is not merely gratifying his own desire, he is enriching her whole system as well as his own through this mutual alchemy.

Before following up the logic of this paragraph, let us turn to the woman and her needs. The drain on her system of providing for another life out of her own tissues, and the substances which pass through her own body, must be very severe unless she is amply provided with all the subtle chemical compounds which are demanded of her. Now there is much evidence that in unmarried women, and in young wives who are debarred from sex union altogether, something approaching a subtle form of starvation occurs ; conversely that women absorb from the seminal fluid of the man some substance, " hormone," " vitamine " or stimulant which affects their internal economy in such a way as to benefit and nourish their whole systems. That semen is a stimulant to a woman was long ago recognized as probable, and is now the opinion of several leading doctors. Reference to this will be found in Havelock Ellis, vol. 5, 1912. See also the paper by Toff in the *Cen-*

tralblatt Gynakologie, April, 1903. Incidentally
the converse is true, and the man who conducts
himself properly during the sex union, and
remains for long in contact with his wife after the
ejaculation is completed, also benefits through
actual absorption from his wife. For this I
have the testimony of a number of men.

If, therefore, the woman who is becoming a
mother, and who is supporting a second life,
feels the need of union with her husband it
is, I maintain, an indication that her nature
is calling out for something not only legitimate
but positively beneficial and required, and that
it should be not only a man's privilege, but his
delight, to unite with his wife at such a time
and under such circumstances.

The maintenance of the right balance of the
internal secretions of the various glands which
re-act on sex activity is important to women
at all times, and particularly during the time
when a woman is becoming a mother. One
of the results of the growth of the child is the
increased activity of the thyroid gland in the
neck, which considerably increases in size.

A general account of the relation of such
glands to a woman's mental and physical balance
is found in Blair Bell's book (*The Sex Complex*,
1916), but he does not deal with the special
aspect of a woman's requirements which forms
the subject of this chapter.

There is, even with the type of woman who does feel the need of, and ardently desires some sex unions with her husband during the long months, almost always a space of time, perhaps as much as two or three months consecutively, when she will have no such desires at all and there are also times of special liability to lose the child through premature birth, when unions should be avoided. Unexpected abortions most usually take place at the dates around the time which would have been a monthly period.

When I consider the evidence which I have before me, which is almost exclusively from the very best type of women, and when I observe that the most generally perfected, and finest women of my acquaintance, and they in particular, desire occasional moderate intercourse during pregnancy, I feel that one has a guide to what is best for the race. In these women and the conduct which their needs inspire, we have an indication of the truest and highest standard of all. The deviations of conduct may at last return from both the grossness of abuse and the reaction from it, and settle in the right and middle path. After the excessively virtuous, and perhaps undersexed type of woman, in contrast to the totally base attitude of the earlier and coarser type of man, has made the thoughtful speed from baseness to an ascetic absence of unions, we should be led back by these well developed and well balanced and noble minded women to the right and middle way. In this the spontaneous impulse of the responsible mother will be the guide for her husband and will benefit all three concerned.

For, let us realize what a profound mystical symbol is enacted when the union is not that of a single man and woman, but of that holy trinity the father, the mother and the unborn child. *Only* during these brief sacred months can the three be united in such exquisite intimacy, and during all these months when the child is forming, it is only in the few infrequent embraces of subdued passion that the husband and father-to-be can come truly close to his child, that he can, through additions to her system from his own, assist the mother in her otherwise solitary task of endowing it with everything its growth demands.

Every woman who is bearing a child by a man whom she loves deeply, longs intensely that its father should influence it as much as it is possible for him to do : in this way *and in this way alone* can he give it of the actual substance of his body.

This view of mine, in the present crude state of scientific knowledge must, of course, be stated as an hypothesis, but it will be proved later on when science is sufficiently subtle to detect the actual microscopic exchange of particles which takes place during proper and prolonged physical contact in the sex union.

Light on my thesis is also shown by the converse : For instance, an interesting suggestion was made by a distinguished medical specialist as a result of his observation of two or three of his own patients, where the prospective mother had desired unions and the husband had denied them thinking it in her interest : the doctor observed that the children seemed to grow up restless and uncontrollable, with a marked tendency to self-abuse. To these two or three instances I have added some which have come under my own observation and, although as yet the evidence is insufficient to support a dogmatic attitude, I incline to think that not only the deprivation of the mother of proper union during pregnancy, but also the after effects of some years of the use of *coitus interruptus* tends to have a similar effect upon later children. That is to say that mothers whose natural desire for union has been denied, and mothers who are congenitally frigid rather tend to produce children with unbalanced sex-feeling liable to yield to self-abuse. Immoderate and excessive desire for sex union during pregnancy so far as I am aware is rare, and where it occurs it should of course be treated as an abnormality.

The mother of the higher type, such as I have indicated in the paragraphs above who does desire unions, will probably only require them infrequently during these months.

It should be obvious, but as the general public often lacks a visualizing imagination, I ought to add, that for the proper consummation of the act of union, particularly during the later months of coming parenthood, the ordinary position with the man above the woman is not suitable and may be harmful. The pair should either lie side by side, or should lie so that they are almost at right angles to each other, so that there is no pressure upon the woman. Or the man should lie on his side behind the woman, which makes penetration easy and safe and free from pressure. I might point out here a fact which is of general importance in all true consummations of the sex union, and that is that all the preliminaries and even the final act of ejaculation itself do not constitute the whole of the truest union. A truth on which I lay great stress, although I have not yet dealt with it fully in any publications, is the fact that an *extremely* important phase of each union is the close and prolonged contact after the culmination takes place. The benefit to both of the pair of remaining in the closest possible physical contact for as long a time as is possible after the crisis is almost incalculable.

A whole chapter could be written upon this theme, and indeed it should be written. In

the union during pregnancy, a woman is by
nature debarred from the complete and intense
muscular orgasm and for her, indeed, the union
must essentially consist almost solely of the
close contact of skin with skin and of the absorption of molecular particles as well as the
resolution of nervous tension as the result of
so close and prolonged a contact.

Among the children known to me personally,
several of the most beautiful were the children
of mothers and fathers who had unions during
the months of their development.   The following
quotation from a young husband may be of
interest in this connection :—

The day before the birth of our baby, we went for a six-
mile walk over country ground, and I slept with my wife the
very night before he was born. . . . We had unions, but
not in the ordinary position ; she would be on her side with
her back to me, and after union would quietly go off to sleep
in my arms, and in the morning would wake with a joyful
and passionate kiss. Now our baby is one of the finest of
babies from all points of view.

As I have seen photographs of the child,
I can endorse the parent's opinions.

Tolstoy's condemnation of any sex contact
while the wife was pregnant or nursing may
have influenced some serious men, but, as in
many other respects, Tolstoy's teaching is
so widely contradictory, and depends so much

upon his own age and state at the time, one cannot but regret the unbalanced influence his literary power has given him.

While this chapter may be taken as an indication that sex union is, in my opinion, not only allowable but advisable for certain types during the time they are carrying a child, nevertheless I do not wish it to be misinterpreted in such a way that a single act of union which is repugnant to the prospective mother should be urged upon her " for her good."

There is undoubtedly a large body of most excellent women who are as individuals distinctly rather undersexed, but who are on the whole good mothers, profoundly well meaning and right minded and virtuous women to whom the time of prospective motherhood is an intensely individual period, during which they feel an active repugnance to any sex union.

Women of this type are not able to give the *completest* dower to their children, but are immensely superior to the average and baser type which forms the majority. If such women do not spontaneously desire unions they should be left unharried by any suggestion that they would benefit by them, and the husbands of such women should, in their own interests, curb any natural impulses which may conflict with the intense feeling of the wife. Husbands, however, should also be aware that such women generally feel as they do because they have never been *wooed* with sufficient grace and tenderness.

To sum up, I am convinced that unless there is any indication of a disease or abnormal appetite in any respect, that the natural wishes and desires of the mother-to-be who is bearing a child should be the absolute law to herself and her husband, for during these months she is on a different plane of existence from the usual one. She is swayed by impulses which science is as yet incapable of analysing or comprehending, and experience has again and again proved that she is wise to satisfy any reasonable desire, whether for the spiritual, bodily or mental contributions to her growing child's requirements or those which would strengthen her own power of supporting that child.

Fortunate indeed is the husband of the best, well-balanced and developed mother-to-be, who with intense emotion shares with him in the closest and most exquisite intimacy, the creating of a life which has every prospect of adding beauty and strength to the world.

CHAPTER XIII

The Procession of the Months

"The mother is the child's supreme parent."
HAVELOCK ELLIS.

AT first invisible, with no outer changes to indicate the vital internal processes, from the moment of conception an intense activity has begun within the mother. Sometimes women are aware of the actual moment of conception, and faintly perceive for the first two or three days sensations too delicate to be called pain and yet intense and penetrating as though of the lightest touch upon the inward and most sensitive consciousness. I have read reports of women, and know one personally, who felt the process of conception, although this will probably be generally received with incredulity. The majority of people are less completely cognisant of the voices of their own organism, and perhaps for two or three months are almost unaware that anything different from the usual course of their life is taking place.

9

If, as seems to me unquestionably the best and happiest relation, the man and woman who are creating a child are doing so deliberately, consciously and with acute interest, a mutual knowledge of the principal stages through which their child passes should add greatly to their interest and the intensity of their feeling.

From the first moment of its conception, indeed often for months before this has been possible, their child is to the loving pair a living entity of whom they may speak.

The active egg cell, which is ready for fertilization, is produced in one or other of the two ovaries, which lie internally and cannot be touched or reached in any way without operating upon the mother ; they have no direct contact with the outer world. These two ovaries each communicate with the central chamber, which is called the womb or uterus and this is a strong muscular organ, into the walls of which the attachment of the minute embryo fastens, and within this chamber the growing embryo gradually fills the space reserved for it. The womb or uterus has a connection with the outer world through the lower mouth called the os, which opens into the vaginal channel. This os or mouth with its rounded lip can just be felt at the end of the vaginal channel.

Fertilization consists in the actual penetration of the egg cell by the male sperm, the nuclei

of which unite. As I have elsewhere described
(*Married Love*, Chap. V) the numbers of male
sperm provided in any act of union outnumber
by millions those actually required, because for
each single fertilization one egg cell combines
with one sperm cell. The egg cell or ovum
is very large in comparison with a single sperm ;
nevertheless it is itself a minute, almost invisible protoplasmic speck, measuring rather
less than 1/120th of an inch in diameter, and
roughly spherical in its shape—a minute pellet
of jelly-like protoplasm with a concentrated
centre or nucleus. The single sperm which
unites with it is a still more minute fleck, and is
little more than a nucleus with a film of protoplasm round it, and a long cilium or hair-like
continuation which it lashes to and fro, and thus
propels itself or swims towards the egg cell.
Judging by analogy, it leaves this tail outside
the egg cell on the mutual fusion. The nucleus
of the sperm and of the egg unite in a very
complex and precise manner. In other organ-
isms, and probably also in human beings, the
entry of a single sperm to the egg cell shuts
out the possibility of other sperms fusing with
them, because directly it has been fertilized,
the egg cell exudes a film of substance which
antagonizes the other sperms, and which ultimately forms a filmy skin around itself.

From the moment of the fusion of the nuclei

of the male and female cells, active changes
and nuclear divisions are in progress. The
egg cell, which is free, travels slowly to the
allotted place in the womb or uterus of the
mother, and there it settles down in the tissue
of the wall and attaches itself. Until it has
attached itself firmly to the wall of the uterus,
conception proper has not finally taken place,
and a fertilized egg cell may be lost through
want of a capacity to attach itself to the womb,
or through some nervous or other disturbance
of the walls of the womb, which throw it off
after it has been attached. The distinction
between the actual moment of fertilization (or
union of the male and female nuclei) and of the
final attachment which secures true conception
is an important one, though frequently overlooked. Sometimes the failure to conceive a
child may not at all be due to lack of fertility
and readiness to unite on the part of the egg
cell and sperm cell, but may be due to some
nervous or other influence on the wall of the
uterus, which consequently throws off the ovum
before it has firmly settled into its place
there.

A few days after conception, and when the
ovum has attached itself to the proper place, a
definite zone of tissue begins to form which,
growing and altering with the growth of the
tiny developing child (which is now called the

embryo), forms a medium of transmission between it and the mother through which pass the substances used and excreted by the embryo in its growth.

After fertilization, intense and rapid activity takes place in the nuclei of the cells, first in the united nucleus of egg and sperm cell, and later in the nuclei of all the resulting division cells. The nucleus of the sperm cell is supposed to contain twelve chromosomes which go through a formal rearrangement and mingling with the corresponding chromosomes in the egg cell. As a result of the complete fusion and intermingling of the male and the female factors on fertilization, all the resulting divisions of cells which follow derive their nuclei partly from the male and partly from the female nucleus of the parents. Thus, if it were possible to trace the history of every tissue cell in the body of your child, we should see that each nucleus of all the myriads that compose its structure would ancestrally consist of part of the many sub-divisions of the nuclei of both father and mother. Thus to speak of one side of the body as being male in its inheritance and the other female, is the most unmitigated nonsense, though this idea formed the basis of a recent book.

The rapidity with which the first cells grow to form tissues, once they have been stimulated by union is very great, and from the ovum, which on the day of fertilization is only 1/120th of an inch in size, the growth is so rapid that it is ten times as big at the end of fourteen days. By that time the length is one-twelfth of an inch, and it weighs one grain. By the thirtieth day the tiny embryo is already one-third of an inch big, and were it practicable, which, of course, it is not, to remove it living from its bed of tissue in the mother's womb and examine it, even with the naked eye, and still more with a magnifying glass, it would be possible to see the rudiments of the legs, head and arms which are to be.

By the fortieth day the embryo is about one inch in length, and the shape of the child, which it is to be, is quite clearly visible. Dark points are to be seen where later it will have eyes, nose and mouth, and there is already a hint of its backbone.

Meanwhile, as may be realized, although to have grown in forty days to the size of an inch from a minute speck 1/120th part of an inch is a great and rapid achievement, nevertheless the existence of a thing one inch big within her makes little outer difference to the mother, and all the earlier weeks and months of the growth of this tiny organism do not yet take more visible effect on the mother's body than to enhance its contour. After the first child this effect is less noticeable, and a woman may be unaware that she is about to become a mother. The first sign in a really healthy woman generally is in the form of her breasts, which sometimes begin to enlarge by the second or third week. It is said that the more healthy and perfectly fitted for motherhood a woman is, the sooner her breasts show signs of the effect of the developing embryo but, particularly with a woman who has already borne a child, there may be no external sign until at least three months have passed.

By the sixth week, the limbs and most essential parts of the child are apparent, and there are the minute indications of the beginning of its future sex organs. It is evident, therefore, that if there is any desire to control the sex of the coming child, it is already too late by the sixth week to do anything, were it ever possible reliably to control sex at any time. It is, therefore, apparent that any passionate desire for a child of one or the other sex which the mother may indulge in when she knows she is about to be a mother, say by the third or fourth month, is futile. It may also be injurious (see Chapter XIV).

By the second month, nearly all the parts are fully apparent, even the eyelids are visible in the embryo and a tiny nose begins to project ; fingers and toes can be seen, and some centres of bone begin to harden, as for instance, in the ribs.

By the third month the embryo reaches an average length of three or more inches, and weighs on an average about $2\frac{1}{2}$ ounces. In this month the sex organs of the future baby are rapidly developing, and indeed are rather unduly prominent in proportion to the other parts which enlarge relatively later.

Between the third and the fourth month, or often not till a little after the fourth month, the active muscular movements of the embryo's limbs can be felt by the mother. The experience of this, like the consciousness of the moment of conception, depends very much upon the sensitiveness and delicate balance of the mother's conscious control of herself.

Some are insensitively, though perhaps comfortably, unaware of what is going on in their systems ; others are conscious, not of what is properly going on, but of what is going wrong in their systems owing to disease or maladjustment; but there are others who, in perfect health, are yet so acutely sensitive and conscious that they can at will detect, as it were, the condition of their whole organs. Such women as these will sooner feel the active movements of the embryo than those who are less perceptive. As a rule, medical practitioners estimate that about half-way between the date of conception and the date of birth, which should be a full nine calendar months, that is to say about $4\frac{1}{2}$ months from the date of conception, muscular movements of the child are detectable and distinct.

In the third month, however, some women are conscious of the most delicate fluttering sensation.

By the end of the third month, a definite enlargement of the mother's body becomes visible, because not only the actual child within her has to be accounted for in the space among her organs, but all the accessory growth of the chamber which accommodates the child in the womb has to find its place, the womb growing rapidly and containing not only the child, but the large amount of fluid by which the child is surrounded, and in which it partly floats. The visible changes in the mother to some extent depend on the proportion of this fluid which develops, some having much more than others, and it is to this rather than to the actual size of the child for the first four or five months that any outward change is due.

About the end of the third month the soft and cartilaginous beginnings of the vertebral column begin to harden in various centres, and afterwards the hardening of the bones (or ossification) slowly spreads throughout the whole skeletal system. For some other bones in the body, however, the hardening is not fully completed by the time of birth.

By the fifth month, the child weighs six to eight ounces, and is from seven to nine inches long. By this time its movements are very active and almost continuous except when it sleeps. It should be trained to sleep at the same time as its mother, and thus give her rest. My phrase " it should be trained to sleep " may arouse incredulous smiles from medical men, even from mothers who have borne children, but it is not impossible to train a child even so young as an unborn embryo, strange as it may sound. From about this month (the fifth) to the time of birth, the child appears to have a strong and definite personality, and sometimes, in some strange and subtle way, it seems possible to communicate with it. If there is that sweet and intense intimacy between mother and father which there should be if the full beauty of parenthood is to be realized, the child is apparently to some extent conscious of the nearness of its father, and I know at least of one or two couples who spoke to their coming child as though it were present, and who, by a touch of the hand could to some extent control and soothe it so that it would sleep during the night when the mother desired to sleep.

About the fifth month the actual nails begin

to grow, although the local preparations for their growth took place much earlier.

After the fifth month, the child grows rapidly in weight, in the sixth month weighing nearly two pounds and during the seventh nearly three.

If it is placed in the best possible position, its head would be directed downwards, and it should be lying so that its arms and legs are tucked in much as a kitten curls up when it is asleep. It will move, however, sometimes completely round, entirely altering its position.

By the eighth month it weighs about four pounds and averages perhaps sixteen inches or so long. It should by this time be very active, so that its movements are not only strongly felt by the mother, but are externally quite perceptible.

By the ninth month, at birth, the child weighs between six and eight or more pounds. It is better for the mother that it should not be too heavy, as, unless she is a large and strongly built woman, the actual weight of the child becomes a great strain upon her, however strong she may be.

A child may be born during the seventh month, and children born during the seventh month live and have sometimes even grown up learned and important men. Sir Isaac Newton is an illustration of a premature child. Usually, however, a seventh month infant is terribly handicapped ; its skin is not yet fully developed, and in many respects it is quite unfitted to face the world.

Many claims are made that a child is seven months at birth which are based on the miscounting of the date of conception or a desire to conceal a pre-marital conception. When one is shown, as one sometimes is, a bouncing, healthy, ordinary baby, and told that it was " a very forward seven months child," those who know can only smile or sigh, according to the circumstances, for an ordinary, healthy, bouncing baby with nails and well formed skin has never yet been generated in seven months.

The seventh month is the time of greatest danger for a late miscarriage, and many have been the diappointments of parents who ardently desired a child, but who lost it through premature birth at the seventh month. I have often wished to know why this should be so, and have found no satisfactory answer or indication of any scientific reason for this, but when revolving all the possibilities of ancestral reminiscence, it occurred to me that possibly our earlier ancestors, ancestors in fact so early as to be scarcely human, were born at the seventh month. I was, therefore, interested to find that for some of the monkeys seven months is the date of normal birth. ᵔPossibly some such ancestral characteristic may make the seventh month a critical time in the development of the human embryo, a time when it inherits the reminiscence of the possibility of separating itself from its mother and coming into the outer world.

The times, moreover, when birth is most liable are those few days in each month which correspond to the regular menstrual flow in the woman, the periods which would have taken place at each twenty-eight days had not the child been developing. It is, therefore, often desirable, particularly for the later months, for the woman to take one or two days of complete rest, or even to remain in bed during that dangerous day or two, so as to minimize the possibility of a miscarriage.

The same applies of course to some extent to the eighth month, but curiously enough, miscarriages in the eighth month appear to be less frequent. It is also popularly said that it is more difficult to rear a child born in the eighth month than one born in the seventh, though this does not appear to be true.

The last week or two of the child's antenatal existence are used by it in finishing itself off ; growing its tiny shell-like nails, losing the downy hair which covered its body earlier in its existence, and in a sense preparing itself, and particularly its skin, for contact with the outer world which is to come. Its movements are very active, and if it is in the most perfect position, the head tends to sink deep down towards the canal approaching the circle of bone through which it will have to pass (see Chapter II).

The question is often asked as to which is the time when the embryo is most sensitive to outward impressions, but as yet there is no sufficient body of evidence to show that at any particular time more than another (unless it be on the actual day of conception, see Chapter II) is the power of influence greater than any other.

Is it possible to pre-arrange, to determine the sex of the child which is voluntarily con-ceived ? Since earliest human experiences have been recorded, this has formed the theme of some writers and thinkers, and a variety of opinions have been expressed, theories pro-pounded, and rules for the production of a girl or boy at will have been given. Each of the views, however, still remains far from being established, and damaging exceptions may be found to every theoretic rule. The impartial observer must feel that we are still unable to control the sex of the child.

There are three main theories on this subject : (a) one is that the nature of the child which will be produced is already pre-determined in the ovum and sperm cell before they have united ; (b) the second theory is that the critical moment which settles the sex of the future offspring is the moment of fertilization and the changes in the nucleus immediately resulting from it; (c) and the third theory is based on the view that the differentiation of the organs, which makes the difference in sex, take place at some stage in the embryo's development after it is already a many-celled organism.

The first named theory lies behind the advice which varies around the theme that according to whether the conception takes place from the egg cell grown in the right or the left ovary and testicle so will the child be a boy or a girl. Instances of the desired child proving to be of the sex " arranged for " by following out some such methods are of comparatively frequent occurrence, but to the scientist are completely counter-balanced by other and negative results.

The second and third theories do not offer the same explicit application in practical advice. But all the practical advice, on whatever basis it is builded, appears to me to be laid on insecure foundations. In my opinion, the complexities of the factors which determine sex are such that it depends much less on the outward and visible nutrition of the mother, than on the inner and almost inscrutable quality of the nutrition of the ovum and spermatozoon before and immediately after fertilization has taken place.

That sex, even in some vertebrate creatures

is actually controllable through nutrition can be easily demonstrated with a batch of frogs' eggs. These can be divided into two portions and by simple differences in the feeding of the young tadpoles male or female frogs can be obtained ; the richly nourished ones produce the female frogs, those on sparser diet the male.   The human embryo, however, developing in and through its mother, will depend to some extent on her diet, but in a much less direct way, for, as all know, the actual nutrition of the system does not depend merely on the quantity and valuable nature of the food taken into the mouth ; it depends equally or even more on the digestive power, on the circulatory system, even on the mentality of the person who eats, and to add still further to the complexity, the tissues and organs of one part of the body may be receiving fully sufficient nutriment, while owing to some hindrance or difficulty some other tissues may be wasting and under-nourished.   It is consequently necessary before we can theorize, to determine, even in the healthiest woman, whether or no a very rich and abundant nutriment is reaching the developing embryo in its earliest and most critical days, for, on the other hand, just in this critical time, a woman relatively ill-fed and in relatively poorer health may be digesting her simple diet well and may be so stimulated as to provide for the minute developing embryo a richer and more nutritious environment than her better fed sister. Consequently, even if, as I incline to believe, the pre-determination of sex depends on the nutriment procurable by the early dividing cells of the embryo, it is still almost beyond the realm of scientific investigation or of human control to determine whether or not the embryo is surrounded with such stimulating food as will produce a girl, or the rather sparser diet which will produce a boy.

CHAPTER XIV

Prenatal Influence

"To leave in the world a creature better than its
parent this is the purpose of right motherhood."
CHARLOTTE GILMAN: *Women and Economics.*

ON the power of the mother directly to
influence her child while it is still unborn, diametrically opposite opinions
have been expressed, and without exaggeration
I think one may safely say that the tendency
of biological science has been to scout the idea
as "old wives' tales" and incredible super-
stition. Fortunate indeed it is that though
our immature and often blundering science has
in many ways permeated and influenced our
lives, yet this denial of profound truth by those
incapable of handling it in the true terms of
science, has not entirely barred this avenue of
power to the mother. Fortunately there are
innumerable children who owe their physical
and spiritual well-being to the profound racial
knowledge still dormant in the true woman.

As I said when I touched upon this question in *Married Love* :—

> Yet all the wisest mothers whom I know vary only in the degree of their belief in this power of the mother. All are agreed in believing that the spiritual and mental condition and environment of the mother does profoundly affect the character and spiritual powers of the child.

Alfred Russel Wallace, the great naturalist and co-discoverer with Darwin of the principle of Evolution, was in many respects a pioneer of unusual foresight and penetrating observation, who thought that the transmission of mental influence from the mother to the child was neither impossible nor even very improbable. In 1893 he published a long letter detailing cases, which he prefaced by saying :—

> The popular belief that prenatal influences on the mother affect the offspring physically, producing moles and other birth-marks, and even malformations of a more or less serious character, is said to be entirely unsupported by any trustworthy facts, and it is also rejected by physiologists on theoretical grounds. But I am not aware that the question of purely mental effects arising from prenatal mental influences on the mother has been separately studied. Our ignorance of the causes, or at least of the whole series of causes, that determine individual character is so great, that such transmission of mental influences will hardly be held to be impossible or even very improbable. It is one of those questions on which our minds should remain open, and on which we should be ready to

receive and discuss whatever evidence is available; and should a *primâ facie* case be made out, seek for confirmation by some form of experiment or observation, which is perhaps less difficult than at first sight it may appear to be.

In one of the works of George or Andrew Combe, I remember a reference to a case in which the character of a child appeared to have been modified by the prenatal reading of its mother, and the author, if I mistake not, accepted the result as probable, if not demonstrated. I think, therefore, that it will be advisable to make public some interesting cases of such modification of character which have been sent me by an Australian lady in consequence of reading my recent articles on the question whether acquired characters are inherited. The value of these cases depends on their differential character. Two mothers state that in each of their children (three in one case and four in the other) the character of the child very distinctly indicated the prenatal occupations and mental interests of the mother, though at the time they were manifested in the child they had ceased to occupy the parent, so that the result cannot be explained by imitation. The second mother referred to by my correspondent only gives cases observed in other families which do not go beyond ordinary heredity.

. . . Changes in mode of life and in intellectual occupation are so frequent among all classes that materials must exist for determining whether such changes during the prenatal period have any influence on the character of the offspring. The present communication may perhaps induce ladies who have undergone such changes, and who have large families, to state whether they can trace any corresponding effect on the character of their children.—*Nature*, August 24 1893, pp. 389, 390.

Yet this suggestive pronouncement of the

world-famous naturalist has never been seriously
followed up by scientists.

I think the time is now ripe for a definite
statement that : *The view that the pregnant
woman can and does influence the mental states of the
future child is to-day a scientific hypothesis which
may be shortly proved.* I make this definite statement, in conjunction with the cognate and
illuminating facts from other fields of research,
a few of which are discussed in the following
pages.

That our mental states can affect, not only
our spirits and our points of view, but actually
the physical structure of our bodies, is demon-
strable in a hundred different ways, and appears
either to be proved or merely suggested according to the bias and temperament of the one to
whom the demonstration is made. But there
is one at least of these physical correlations
which can be demonstrated with scientific
thoroughness, and which proves beyond doubt
that the mental state of the mother *has* a reaction upon her infant even after it has severed
its physical connection with her, and is a baby
of a few months old. This fact is that a nursing
mother who is subjected to a violent shock
which results in a paroxysm of temper or of terror
in her own mind, conveys the physical result
of this to her infant when next she nurses it,
so that the child has either an attack of indi-

gestion or a fit. The effect of the mother's mental state is transmitted by the influence on the milk, the chemical composition of which is subtly altered by her nervous paroxysm, and which thus acts as a poison to the infant.

A much more subtle and closer correlation must exist between the mother's mental states and the child when it is still not yet free and independent in the outer environment of the world but while it finds in her body its entire environment, its protection and the resources out of which it is building its own structure, while the blood and the tissues of her body form its whole world, while through them and through them alone can it obtain all its nourishment.

True, the result of the mental state of the mother which we can see is, apparently, merely the physical result on the child's digestion of the milk which has become poisoned : but to stop at this point like a jibbing mule, and to refuse to take the further step in the argument because the child is yet too young for us to understand its resulting mental states, which reason indicates must be correlated with its poisoned digestive system, is to defraud the mind of the logical conclusion of a sequence of ideas.

The argument is as follows :—

(a) The mother's intense *mental* experience

and consequent nervous paroxysm has a physical result upon the composition of her milk (presumably, therefore, upon other portions of her body, though this is irrelevant for the moment);

(b) This physically altered milk has a physical effect upon the infant who shows other and more extreme forms of physical distress;

(c) This physical distress must obviously to some greater or lesser degree, affect the child's nervous system ; and (which is the point where the old-fashioned will break off);

(d) Consequently the child's mental state will be affected—although it is too young to translate this into conscious forms.

Were I to make this the main thesis of my book, examples of the effect of mental states on bodily functions could be readily multiplied, and illustrations drawn from facts quoted in other connections could be found in a great number of medical works. I here bring together a few which when placed in juxtaposition offer if not proof, yet such strong support of my theme as to place it in the realm of the scientifically ascertainable. For instance, Blair Bell in *The Sex Complex*, 1916, says :—

Religious manias may lead to ideas which fill the patient with abhorrence of sexual intercourse, and in this way directly interfere with the genital functions. There is indeed no doubt whatsoever that the mind influences function just as function influences the mind; for example, it has been shown that fright leads to an immediate increase in the output of suprarenin, and we know well from constant clinical observations that hypothyroidism leads to mental depression (pp. 209 and 210).

and Havelock Ellis in *The Psychology of Sex*, vol. 5, 1912, says :—

We can, again, as suggested by Féré, very well believe that the maternal emotions act upon the womb and produce various kinds and degrees of pressure on the child within, so that the apparently active movements of the *fœtus* may be really consecutive on unconscious maternal excitations. We may also believe that, as suggested by John Thomson, there are slight incoördinations *in utero*, a kind of developmental neurosis, produced by some slight lack of harmony of whatever origin and leading to the production of malformations. We know, finally, that, as Féré and others have repeatedly demonstrated during recent years by experiments on chickens, etc., very subtle agents, even odors, may profoundly affect embryonic development and produce deformity. But how the mother's psychic disposition can, apart from heredity, affect specifically the physical conformation or even the psychic disposition of the child within her womb must remain for the present an insoluble mystery, even if we feel disposed to conclude that in some cases such action seems to be indicated.

Direct evidence of the physical aspect of my thesis is found in the fact quoted by Marshall in *The Physiology of Reproduction*, 1910, p. 566 :—

So also it has been found that immunity from disease may be acquired by young animals being suckled by a female which had previously become immune, the antibody to the disease being absorbed in the ingested milk.

Further argument upon these lines might well be brought forward in favour of the view that the potential mother, during the months whilst she is acting as the child's total environment in all physical ways, is also through her mental states and conditions affecting the child's ultimate mentality and artistic and spiritual powers.

This subtle control exerted over the formation of the child may be visualized as more like some effect parallel to the remote influences of the internal secretions in controlling the other organs of the body than the more mechanical picture of things visualized by the Mendelians and those who concentrate on the purely physical and material aspects of heredity as related to chromosome structure.

The tendency in recent years in biological work has been far too much to lay stress upon the curiously mathematical laws Mendel discovered, and consequently to concentrate attention upon the physical chromosomes as containing the factors which carry hereditary qualities. Physiologists are now making an attempt to bring back into the treatment of life a more rational outlook, and nothing has con-

tributed more to the scientific basis of this than
the recent following up of the suggestions made
so long ago as 1869 by Brown-Séquard. Since
Starling named the internal secretions Hormones
(see the Croonian Lecture, 1905) they have been
much discussed by physiologists and some
medical men (see for instance the recent work of
Blair Bell, *The Sex Complex*, 1916 already quoted).

To form a rough mental picture of what
is happening one must combine the physiological and the mechanical outlooks. One then
obtains the idea that the mother is, through
her mental states, affecting and to some extent
controlling the production of the various
internal secretions, and other more subtle
and still undetected influences from various
organs upon other organs, and that, in so doing
she is making the environment for the various
hereditary factors, in which their potentialities
find it possible to develop or to be suppressed
according to the circumstances which she thus
creates. As is now beginning to be realized,
we all have an immense number of latent potentialities, which may lie dormant and develop
only under suitable circumstances.

Thus in my view the mother may actually
and in every sense fundamentally influence and
control the character of her child, working
through the remote effects of internal secretions
which play on the complex material factors of

hereditary qualities which form the material basis of the child's potentialities.

Thus both heredity and environment have a vital part to play in building character, *but greater than either is the subtler environment within the prospective mother created by her during the nine antenatal months.*

Sometimes people who would otherwise like to believe that a mother has this power, are deterred by their own experience or that of others, who have, under conditions of distress and un-favourable circumstances, had children whose dispositions seem not to have suffered, but appear as sunny and happy as a child ap-parently conceived under more favourable cir-cumstances. Here, however, one is immediately faced by the difficulties of accurate observation entailing a large number of data which tend to cancel out ; for the mother who may per-sonally have been below her usual standard of health and spirits while bearing the child may, nevertheless, actually be in such a good physical condition, or be a member of such a sound, healthy stock that the child's heredity was better than that of the average human being, and consequently that the child itself was provided with a healthy well-run body.

While to contrast with it and apparently to refute my thesis, there may be a mother full of the most ardent hopes and buoyant spirit,

looking forward with supreme joy to the advent
of her baby, doing all she can to give it every
beautiful mental impression and physical health,
whose work may yet be undone by some cruel
chance, such as venereal infection, or some local
malformation which has resulted in weakness
in, let us say, the child's digestion. We all
know how peevish mere indigestion will make
anybody. Or she, the well-intentioned and outwardly well-circumstanced mother may, unknown
to herself, have been battling against the cruel
handicap in some racial, heritable defect in her
husband ; the child, therefore, may, with all
her efforts, yet fail to be joyous owing to the
too strong physical bias which chance or
heritable disease has given it.

The existence of such apparently conflicting
and contradictory individual instances in no way
refutes my main thesis, which is that granted
equal conditions of clean and wholesome ancestry,
granted equally favourable conditions of health
and nutrition for the mother during her period
of carrying the child, that that child benefits
and is superior to the other who has had the
advantage of a happy mother's conscious effort
to transmit to it a wide and generally intellectual and spiritual interest in the great and
beautiful things of the world.

This fact is often illustrated in the different
children of the same parents. Of children

born under as nearly identical circumstances as may be possible within a year or two of time, the one may have a totally different disposition with totally different qualities from the other. The chance of birth, the inheritance of the innumerable possible characteristics latent in both parents might be sufficient to account for this were chance alone at work, but very often information may be obtained from the observant mother which correlates her own state while carrying the child with the after condition of the child itself.

One rather striking instance of such a correlation is by a curious chance known to me, and should be of general interest.   Oscar Wilde, whose genius was sullied by terrible sex crimes, which he expiated in prison, is known to all the world as a type whose distressing perversion is a racial loss.   His mother once confided to an old friend that all the time she was carrying her son Oscar, she was intensely and passionately desiring a daughter, visualizing a girl, and, so far as was possible, using all the intensity of purpose which she possessed to have a girl, and that she often in after years blamed herself bitterly, because she felt that possibly his perverted proclivities were due to some influence she might have had upon him while his tiny body was being moulded.

Evidence upon this subject of the power of

otherwise of the mother to influence her coming child is wanted, and it is very difficult to obtain, partly because of the reticence of those who have been through the dim and secret mysteries of motherhood, and partly because their accuracy cannot well be tested until after the child has reached maturity. In these after years the mother is likely to be swayed by the course the child's life has taken, into unconsciously laying stress upon one or other point which may seem correlated with its after achievements.

Evidence, however, in the form of notes kept during the time the mother is carrying the child which may be compared with the child's life in later years are very valuable, and, if any readers have such with which they would entrust me, a sufficient body of such evidence might possibly be accumulated to assist materially in the formation of a strong spiritual asset in the creation of the best possible human beings.

The father who desires to influence his child must do so through the mother : had clever men more generally realized this we should have heard less of the lament that clever men so often have stupid sons.

Of the more physical aspects of the mother's power to influence the form of the development of her growing child we have abundant evidence. If the mother is starved, and by starved I mean

less the actual starvation from want of food
than the subtler starvation of improper food or
food lacking in the truly vital elements, then
the child visibly suffers. For instance, rickets,
a disease of grave racial significance to which
reference has already been made (see Chapter
II), is due to the lack of certain necessary
elements in the food.

A simple diet, the simpler the better, is sufficient
adequately to provide all the essentials of nourishment for the mother and her coming child,
and much indeed may be done for the general
health and beauty of the child by providing the
mother with the best form of material from
which the embryo may build itself. The use
of foods containing large quantities of vitamine
(real butter and oranges, for instance, are specially
good) is very advisable. They are not only
enriching in their action in assisting true assimi-
lation of other foods, but they probably tend to
make good the general drain on the mother's
vitality which would naturally take place were
she not amply provided with these most subtle
ingredients, which, though present in such
minute quantities in fresh food, are yet of incalculable value. The effect of proper and
specially adapted dieting, not only on the health
of the mother, but also on the beauty and general
vigour of the child, is a thing which is particularly expressed by various writers who have

followed up the early experiments on diet made
by Dr. Trall.

There is also Dr. Alice Stockham's book,
Tokology, to which I have previously drawn
attention. Although, as I then said, it contains
errors of a comparatively trivial nature such as
calling carbonaceous material " carbonates,"
which may have been sufficient to prejudice the
scientific mind against the rest of her work, it
contains the profound and valuable message Mr.
Rowbotham published in England in 1841,
amplified, and to some extent enriched by this
woman doctor's experience.

Those lovers who ardently desire their child
and have a mental picture of it long before its
birth may delight in speaking of it to each other
as though it were, as indeed it is, alive. For
this a name is required, but in order to avoid
the danger suggested on page 141, it is wiser
perhaps to choose the name of both a girl and
a boy, the name which the child would be called
by according to its sex after birth, and, while it
is still unseen, to link the two together in
speaking of the coming child.

Sometimes for private reasons a girl in particular or a boy in particular may be desired,
but the well-balanced mind of a parent, particularly of the first child, should welcome either a
son or a daughter, each of whom has its peculiar
charms, and neither of whom can be described

as more valuable than the other. Our false
estimate of boys as superior is largely due to
economic conditions and the custom of male
entail. This should, and of course will, be
altered. It is the first *child*, whether boy or
girl is no matter, who is " the first-born " with
all that that connotes in rapture and wonder to
its parents.

Owing to the fact that more boys are born
than girls, there is always the greater chance
of the birth of a boy than a girl. From this
point of view it would appear that girls are
more precious, but boys are oftener ailing and
feeble and difficult to rear, so that it is perhaps
well that more of them should be born than
of their stronger sisters.

Throughout its coming, the little one should
be thought of in such a way that it will be
equally welcome whichever its sex, and thus be
given the best chance of developing fully and
naturally in its own way.

CHAPTER XV

Evolving Types of Women

Deliverance is not for me in renunciation. I feel the embrace of freedom in a thousand bonds of delight.

Thou ever pourest for me the fresh draught of thy wine of various colours and fragrance, filling this earthen vessel to the brim.

No, I will never shut the doors of my senses. The delights of sight and hearing and touch will bear thy delight.

Yes, all my illusions will burn into illumination or joy, and all my desires ripen into fruits of love.

TAGORE: *Gitanjali.*

ONE of the great sources of disharmony in our social life is the extent of the extraordinary ignorance about ourselves which still persists. From this spring our conflicting opinions and diametrically opposed views, and also the apparently self-contradictory evidence on almost any point of fundamental importance which is brought before the public.

In no respect is there more conflict of opinion than concerning the age at which a woman should marry and become a mother. On the one hand, we have advocates of very early motherhood, and they point to the fact that a girl of seventeen is often already a woman and strongly sexed ; they point to the hackneyed statement " that a girl matures sooner than a boy " ; they point to the fine and healthy babies which very young mothers may bear and to the greater pliability and ease of birth, and these facts and their arguments may appear conclusive. On the other hand, the actual experience of many people conflicts with these apparently justified conclusions.

All the highly evolved races tend to prolong childhood and youth. All tend to replace early marriage by later marriage and parenthood to the obvious advantage of the race.

Marriage and parenthood at fourteen, fifteen and sixteen, which once were common in almost every country, are being replaced by later marriage and parenthood. As Finot 1913 says :—

A mystic chain appears to attach the age for love to the consideration enjoyed by women. In the Far East, woman is offered very young to the passion of man, and disappears from existence at the time her contemporaries are just beginning to live. Love, for this very reason, has a purely sensual stamp, degrading to man and to woman. The lengthening of the age of love elevates the dignity, and at the same time increases the longevity, of woman. Beyond the age of thirty or forty the woman, dead to love, was fit only for religion or witchcraft. Her life was shattered. Prematurely aged she went out of the living world. The prolonged summer of Saint-Martin in women will doubtless have consequences which we should be wrong to fear. There is a solidarity of ages. The cares bestowed on the child benefit the old man. The enlarge-ment of the age of maturity allows the child longer to enjoy the years of life that are intended to form bodies and souls. . . . The sentimental life of the country has undergone similar results. Balzac, in proclaiming the right to love on the part of the woman of thirty, aroused in his contemporaries astonish-ment bordering on indignation. In his day, was not a man of forty-four considered an old man ? [1] Let us not forget that forty or fifty years before Balzac, a philosopher like Charles Fourier, despairing of the sentimental fate of young girls who had not found a husband before the age of . . . eighteen years, claimed for them the right to throw propriety to the winds. According to the author of the *Théorie des Quatre-Mouve-ments,*[2] this was almost the critical age (*Problems of the Sexes,* transl. Jean Finot 1913).

The relative ages of husband and wife also have their influence, but should, to some extent, depend more on their *physiological* age than on their actual years. They should, however, not be widely different. As Saleeby says :—

The greater the seniority of the husband, the more widow-hood will there be in a society. Every economic tendency, every demand for a higher standard of life, every agggravation for the struggle for existence, every increment of the burden of the defective-minded, tending to increase the man's age

---

[1] Balzac : *Physiologie du Mariage.*
[2] Charles Fourier, Leipzig, 1808

at marriage, which, on the whole, involves also increasing his seniority—contributes to the amount of widowhood in a nation.

We, therefore, see that, as might have been expected, this question of the age ratio in marriage, though first to be considered from the average point of view of the girl, has a far wider social significance. First, for herself, the greater her husband's seniority, the greater are her chances of widowhood, which is in any case the destiny of an enormous preponderance of married women. But further, the existence of widowhood is a fact of great social importance because it so often means unaided motherhood, and because, even when it does not, the abominable economic position of women in modern society bears hardly upon her. It is not necessary to pursue this subject further at the present time. But it is well to insist that this seniority of the husband has remoter consequences far too important to be so commonly overlooked (*Woman and Womanhood*, 1912).

I have observed many girls, who were in every true sense of the word girls (that is unconscious of personal sex feeling, still growing in bodily stature and still developing in internal organization) until they were nearly thirty years of age. In my opinion, the girl who is thoroughly well-balanced, with an active brain, a well-developed normally sexed body, natural artistic and social instincts is not more than a child at seventeen, and to marry her at that age or anything like it is to force her artificially, and to wither off her potentialities.

The type of woman who really counts in our modern civilization is, as a rule, not of age until she is nearly thirty. Not only does she *not* mature sooner than a boy ; she matures actually later than a large number of men. I have now accumulated a wide and varied amount of evidence in favour of the view which I here propound, namely, that there is a most highly evolved type of woman in our midst. This type, which it will be agreed is the most valuable we possess, encompasses women of a wide range of potentialities ; they have beautiful entirely feminine bodies, with all feminine and womanly instincts well developed, with a normal, indeed a rather strong, sex instinct and acute personal desires which tend to be concentrated on one man and one man alone. I will provisionally call this the late maturing type, for such a woman is generally incapable of real sex experience till she is about twenty-seven or thirty. I think that she is in line with the highest branch of our evolution, that she represents the present ffower of human development, and that through her and her children the human race nas the best hope of evolving on to still higher planes— but, and this is very important, she is not fitted for marriage until she is at least twenty-seven, probably later, her best child-bearing years may be after she is thirty-five, and her most brilliant and gifted children are likely to be born when she is about forty.

Personal evidence, and also facts in the in-

teresting letters sent me by my readers have
brought to my knowledge the existence of an
important proportion of women who are absolutely unconscious of personal localized sex
feeling until they are nearly or over thirty—
one woman was nearly fifty before she felt and
knew the real meaning of sex union though many
years married.

From outward observation of the general
physique of such of these women as I have
seen face to face, I may say that, as a rule, they
retain their youth long ; they retain also a buoyancy and vitality which, if they are properly
treated, and have the good fortune to be married
at the right time to the right man, may remain
with them almost throughout their lives. Such
women not only prolong their girlhood, they
defer their age. Such women have, of course,
throughout the centuries appeared from time to
time, and I fancy have generally in the past,
and still often in the present, suffered acutely
through marrying too young. When they marry
too young they tend, by the forcing of their
feelings, by the deadening through habit of
their potentialities, by the trampling on the
unfolded possibilities within them, to be turned
artificially into a " cold type of woman."

Women now older tell me of the fact that
for the first years of their married life they
could give no response, but when they were

respectively twenty-nine, thirty, thirty-one or more, they began first to feel they were truly women. Young husbands have written to me of their distress that their wives (aged about twenty to twenty-three), delightful girls in every respect, seemed utterly incapable of any response in the marital orgasm. Sometimes this depends on her conformation, but such an incapacity I often attribute to the girl's marriage being premature. When she is twenty-seven or twenty-eight perhaps her internal development will be complete, and she will then be ripe for the full enjoyment of marriage : but if instead of a considerate husband she marries one who merely uses her, she stands little chance ever of knowing the proper relation of wifehood and motherhood.

These facts which I could vary with details from individual experiences, in my opinion, indicate a profound truth in the development of the human race. It is this : not only do the higher races of human beings have a prolonged childhood and youth, but the most highly evolved, mentally, physically and racially, of our girls have not finished their potential growth into maturity until they are in the neighbourhood of thirty years of age.

Does this then mean that all marriage should be deferred till so late ? By no means, nor is the above conclusion any reflection on the type of girl who ripens much more quickly. I

fully recognize that from the point of view of
their sex potentialities some girls are complete
women at seventeen or eighteen, and that they
may then be very strongly sexed indeed. Such
women should marry young.

The marked differentiation of type of these
very notably different women can be traced
through many other aspects of their lives.
I consider, for instance, the type of whom I
spoke in Chapter XII (who has a natural desire
for union, representing the highest and most
complex human union, the union of three)
belongs very frequently to the late maturing
and the most highly evolved form of femininity.

It should be recognized that there are among
us not only different races, but that in the same
stock, sometimes in the same family of apparently no specially mixed ancestry, we may find
one or more members of the late maturing,
others of the early maturing type. Sometimes
of two sisters, the elder may perhaps be still
in mind a girl while her younger sister is a
woman, as can be observed by any one with a
large circle of acquaintances. It would be
well, I think, if humanity, whose proper study
is mankind, were at least to know themselves
sufficiently well to realize the existence of such
different types, and their possible potential
value as well as their differing needs. The
energy at present wasted in the acrid statement

of conflicting views would be so much better
spent on the careful recording and recognizing
of varying types.

❧The advice to marry young, which is in every
respect socially wise and physiologically correct
for some, should not be hurled indiscriminately
at all women, because for the late maturing
such advice is socially disadvantageous and
physiologically wrong.

I am now ready to consider the question of
the proper age for motherhood about which an
immense variety of opinion is expressed. The
general tendency has been, even in the last
few years, to raise the age at which a girl may
marry, and to raise the age which the medical
profession advises as the earliest suitable for
motherhood. But still one often hears of elders,
whom one would in other respects like to follow,
advising the early bearing of children.

Now I should like every potential parent to
consider what type of child they want. Do
they want to secure healthy, jolly little animals
with no more brains than are sufficient to see
them creditably through life ? If so, let them
have their children very early. Such healthy
sound people with no special gifts are valuable,
and there is much work in the world for them to
to do. On the other hand, do they want to
take the risk for their child of a possibly less
robust body, but with the possibility, indeed, in

healthy families, almost the certainty, of an immensely greater brain power, and a more strongly developed temperament? Then let them have their children late. And if a man desires to have a child who may become one of the *master* minds whose discoveries, whose artistic creations, whose ruling power stamps itself upon the memory of our race, whose name is handed down the ages, then let the father who desires such a child mate himself with the long-young late-maturing type of woman I have just described, and let her bear that child some time between the age of thirty-five and forty-five.

How often one hears some version of the phrase : " Yes, it is so sad, poor, dear Lord So-and-So, a charming man, but no brains at all ; his younger brother such a brilliant man ; but that is always the way, the eldest sons in the aristocracy do seem to get the gift of property balanced by the lack of brains." Now I enquire, and I should like my readers to enquire, into the secret of this phenomenon, which is by no means universal, but is sufficiently common to be endorsed. In my opinion, the interpretation of this fact is that the earlier children were born when the mother was still too young to endow them with brains, particularly if the mother was one of the gifted and cultivated women of the late-maturing type.

This also leads me to consider another generality which is frequently used as an argument by those who oppose conscious and deliberate parenthood. Some people say that by the direct control of the size of the family to a small limited number which the parents definitely desire, we would be eliminating genius from our midst, and their argument runs : Look at Nelson, he was a fifth son ; look at Sir Walter Scott, he was a third son ; and so on. This to the uncritical seems conclusive, and many people of great capacity, ideals and heart, who otherwise would be wholly on my side in my claim that every child born shall be deliberately desired, and that all other conceptions shall be consciously prevented, are swayed by this argument and say : " Yes, your position would be obviously the right one for the race if it were not that later children are so often the better." I turn, therefore, to a consideration of the life histories of these men's mothers. Why was Nelson the genius of his family ? Because his mother was too young to bear geniuses at the time she was bearing her elder children. But this is not yet a sufficiently accurate consideration of the subject ; I want to know also of which type the mother was, for, in my opinion, the right age for the parenthood of a woman depends also on the type to which she belongs, whether the early maturing or the late maturing. If

she knows herself to be the latter, after it is
patent, as it must become patent to every one
once the idea is placed before them, that such
women are in our midst, then that woman and
her husband should usually defer parenthood until
she has reached at least thirty years of age.
If this were done, then not the fourth, fifth or
seventh but the first child would stand a very
great chance of being a world leader, a powerful
mind, perhaps even a genius. First children
have been geniuses (Sir Isaac Newton was an
only child) ; all depends on the age, the conscious
desire, the general type and the surrounding
conditions during prenatal state of her infant,
of the mother who bears him and the father
from whom he also inherits potentialities.

A few investigations bearing on the effect
of the parent's age have been published by the
Eugenics Society and some individuals, but
none of these appear to me to be of any value,
for none take into account the necessary data
concerning the type of the mother which I
here point out, and in all the calculations
crude errors occur.

The best woman, with comparatively few
exceptions, is already and will still more in the
future be the woman who, out of a long, healthy
and vitally active life, is called upon to spend
but a comparatively small proportion of her
years in an *exclusive* subservience to motherhood.

A woman should have eighty to ninety active years of life ; if she bears three or perhaps four children, she will, even if she gives up all her normal activities during the later months of pregnancy and the earlier of nursing, still have cut out of her life but a very small proportion of its total. She should, indeed, after she once is a mother, always devote a proportion of her energies to the necessary supervision of her children's growth and education, but with the increasing number of schools and specialists, nurses, teachers and instructors of all sorts, the individual mother has much less of the purely physical labour of her children than formerly. That this is not only so, but is *approved* by the State can be seen at once by imagining a working class mother insisting on keeping her child at home all day under her personal supervision—the School Inspector would step in and take the child from her for a certain number of hours every day. But this book is primarily for middle and upper class women, and for them motherhood increasingly should mean a *widening* of their interests and occupations.

The counter-idea still expressed, even by leading doctors and others, is that the whole capability of the individual mother should be devoted solely to contributing to her children. This is exemplified in the recent statement of Blair Bell : " A normal woman, therefore, would not exploit her capabilities for individual gain, but for the benefit of her descendants." This view is a false one and is based on a narrow vision.

This pictures an endless chain of fruitless lives all looking ever to some supreme future consummation which never materializes. By means of this perpetual sinking of woman's personality in a mistaken interpretation of her duty to the race, every generation is sacrificed in turn. The result has not been productive of good, happiness or beauty for the majority. No ; the individual woman, normal or better than the average, *should* use her intellect for her individual gain in creative work ; not only because of its value to the age and community in which she lives, but also for the inheritance she may thus give her children and so that when her children are grown up they may find in their mother not only the kind attendant of their youth, but their equal in achievement. With a woman of capacities perhaps still exceptional, but by no means so rare as some men writers would like to pretend, the pursuit of her work or profession and honourable achievement in it is not at all incompatible with but is highly beneficial to her motherhood. As Charlotte Gilman says :—

No, the maternal sacrifice theory will not bear examination.

As a sex specialized to reproduction, giving up all personal activity, all honest independence, all useful and progressive economic service for her glorious consecration to the uses of maternity, the human female has little to show in the way of results which can justify her position. Neither by the enormous percentage of children lost by death nor the low average health of those who survive, neither physical nor mental progress, give any proof to race advantage from the maternal sacrifice—*Women and Economics.*

CHAPTER XVI

Birth and Beauty

" Days and nights pass and ages bloom and fade like flowers. Thou knowest how to wait.

Thy centuries follow each other perfecting a small wild flower."

TAGORE : *Gitanjali*.

WHEN all goes well and there is no accidental hastening of the birth by shock or jar which dislodges the child too soon, the birthday finds its place in the ordinary rhythm of the woman's existence. We speak generally of the " nine months " during which the child is borne by its mother, but this nine months is a fictitious number depending on our calendar months, and the developing child is actually ten lunar months within its mother. Just as the average almost universal period of the woman's rhythm has twenty-eight days cycle, so on this number of days does the circle of months leading to birth depend. Ten months of twenty-eight days each is the full period of development, at the close of which the child seeks its exit through birth. As a rule the day of birth corresponds to some extent, if not quite accurately, to the former rhythm of her menstrual waves.

An interesting paper containing various scientific data (not all of which are universally accepted) is to be found in the *Anat Anzeiger* of 1897 by Beard. What is actually the spring behind this rhythm is as yet largely unknown, but recent work on the internal secretions from the ovary such as was described by Starling in the *Croonian Lecture*, 1905 (who quotes Marshall and Jolly and other workers), appears to indicate that this function like so many others in our system is due to the activities of certain glands yielding internal secretions. These, penetrating the whole system, have a controlling influence upon activities remote from their source.

For the birth itself, the mother should be in experienced hands, preferably those of a highly trained and certified midwife or maternity nurse such as Queen Charlotte's or the London Hospital supplies, one who is experienced in all that has to be done in normal, healthy circumstances, and who can detect at once any necessity for specialized help. If the mother has lived rightly and wisely, dieted as I suggest and is properly formed (as, of course, should be assured through examination some time before the birth is expected), the birth should be, how ever terrible an experience, yet one which is safely passed.

In the days which follow she will have much to endure, and instead of the peace and quietness which she expected, she will find that she has constant disturbances incidental to the nursing of one who is, in essentials, a surgical case.

Possibly due to the inconveniences involved in staying in bed, there is a tendency at present to encourage the mother to get up and at least walk about the room and be up for an hour or two within ten days or less of the date of the birth. Almost every one with whom I have come in contact, advises this, and in a certain school, particularly those who go in for what is called "Twilight Sleep," there is not only an effort to get the mother up early, but a pride on the part of the mother and her advisers when she gets up perhaps within two or three days of the birth.

Some women who have had a good many children boast of how they are up and about in ten days. I glance critically at all who tell me that, examining both their figures and their general appearance. *Only one woman of all who have ever discussed this matter with me urged the entirely old-fashioned month in bed following the birth. But, and this is very important, she was the only one who, having had many children, at the same time had done most notable and arduous brain work, and also retained her youthful figure and general appearance.*

This quite exceptional and old-fashioned advice is what I would hand on to women to-day. The modern craze for getting up quickly is absolutely wrong, and has a fundamentally deleterious effect on the general health of our women. I should go so far as to say that not only should a woman stay in bed the entire month, but that she should for two weeks longer scarcely put her foot to the ground. She may lie out of doors or on sofas, but, after a birth, *she should lie about for the whole of six weeks.*

This may startle my readers. I, who look so keenly into the future, who am so progressive, so modern and so desirous of the great and rapid evolution of women, to return to the old custom of our grandmothers, and demand, not only the month in bed, to ask even more, that there should be six weeks spent practically lying about all the time ! Is this not an anachronism ? No. It will be observed that throughout this and my other books, my advice always has a biological basis, depending on the actual structure or the history of our bodies, and there is a very profound and physiological basis for the advice I now give. It is this—that not only during the birth is the whole system of the mother to some extent jarred and shaken ; she suffers in all her nerves the sudden relief from

the strain upon her muscles and in the whole
readjustment of her system an extremely profound shock, and the treatment for shock entails
rest. More than that, the womb which lies
centrally and is so important an organ in her
body, so enormously enlarged during the last
months through which the child inhabited it,
returns to its permanent size slowly ; its strong,
muscular walls tensely contract, but this con-
traction which reduces its size very much in
the first day or two does not complete itself,
does not bring the tissues back to the size which
they will afterwards permanently maintain, *until
six weeks have elapsed*. For the whole of six
weeks, therefore, the womb will be larger and
heavier than normal and with a tendency to
get out of place, while all the muscles of the
body wall are weakened and out of condition
by being so long stretched. A woman, therefore, should not put any strain on her muscles
like standing or walking or taking any active
exercise before the six weeks has elapsed, though
she should, lying both on her back and on her
face, do exercises calculated to restore the strength
of these muscles and fit them to take on their
work directly she rises. One exercise, particularly valuable and but little known, is to raise
the diaphragm without breathing. This can
be done during the six weeks in bed, but is
particularly valuable on first rising and standing

or walking. This internal pull upwards of all the organs strengthens both the internal and the outer body wall muscles. Such control deliberately and frequently exerted throughout the day does more perhaps than any one other thing to retain a slender well-formed trunk. It has also a curiously bracing and exhilarating mental effect, and as the action can be done at any time unobserved, its effect can be utilized at will. The ancient Greeks laid great stress on the value of control of the diaphragm.

It may be argued that during the time the child was within it the womb was very much larger than it is after birth, and nevertheless then active walking exercise was recommended. Yes : but during that time the womb was supported by the increased tension on the front muscles of the body wall against which it pressed and was thus assisted in maintaining its position ; but after birth, while it is so very much smaller than quite recently it has been, and, at the same time, while still much larger than normal, and more than the weakened internal muscles are prepared to support, it is no longer held firm by the tense body wall, for the body wall is now limp, crumpled and almost incapable of supporting any strain. If, therefore, the woman stands too soon, the inner organs which are again beginning to find their natural place—the long digestive tract and other organs—tend to flop downwards, to bulge out the still loose and strained abdominal muscles, and press the still too heavy womb out of its normal position, the position to which it must return, and must permanently take up if the woman is to have her general health maintained throughout the rest of her life. Hence, before she sets foot to the ground she must lie the nature-decreed six weeks, and meanwhile *exercise* the abdominal muscles so as to prepare them to act properly.

When I see and hear of women either forced or lured or eagerly getting out of bed in ten days or a week after child birth, I wonder what will happen to all those women ten or fifteen years hence. They will be fortunate if they do not have what is now so increasingly prevalent, namely some form of displacement of the womb with all its attendant miseries of handicapped motherhood and wifehood. I maintain that it is nothing short of cruelty and criminality to allow the modern woman to get up quickly in the way she does. It may possibly be claimed by some of the foolish and hardy pioneers of getting up rapidly, that when she is a middle-aged or elderly woman she will not be suffering from the slow relaxations and displacements which result from putting pressure too soon on abdominal muscles unprepared to bear the strain. This will not make things safe for the average woman however. It is not realized how appalling is the prevalence of womb displacements among the lower working-class women, those who are forced by circumstances to get up in a week or ten days and go back to work. I think the modern increase in displacements in middle and upper class women is partly to be traced to the tendency to get up too soon, and also to the impatient practitioner's use of instruments to hasten a birth which would come naturally in good time. When once the perineal and inner supporting muscles have been torn, they are too often mended superficially, but inner tears are left which make the perineum an insufficient support for the womb, of which the result is its slow and gradual dropping out of place, which some years afterwards may acutely handicap the unfortunate woman.

In the name of all the fond and happy mothers that I hope the future may contain, I would urge every one who possibly can to *insist* on having six weeks of " lying in." This is not only in the interests of general health but of beauty. Too long have we become tolerant of the hideous formation of the body which is common in older women. We have domesticated some animals [1] solely for our own purposes, and they are hideous indeed. Why should we

[1] The sow normally breeding once a year, artificially forced to breed two or three times a year. Its appearance is proverbial.

women permit a comparable standard for ourselves ? Why not insist on at least as much
care as is devoted to the race-horse ? Why
not take a period of rest after the great effort
of maternity proportionately as long as a she-
wolf or tigress takes in her cave, fed by her
mate while she lies about and plays with her
cubs ? [1] The standard of beauty of the racing
mare, of the wild tigress or she-wolf is slender
and not markedly different from that of its
virgin state. Such a standard, and not that of
the over-taxed, man-used, domesticated animals
should be that on which we women should insist.

In this connection should be mentioned one
other way in which the following of Nature
and obedience to her law works for good. In
the next chapter I mention the baby's right
to be fed by nature's food, and while the
infant is nursing from its mother it stimulates
contractions in the womb which very much
assist in bringing it to its right size and position,
and so the act of nursing benefits not only the
infant but its mother.

A number of researches by various experts
have been made, which proves that the womb
reacts to the stimulus of suckling by the child.
Pfister (*Beit. z. Geb. u. Gyn.*, 1901, vol. v, p. 421),
for instance, found that very definite contrac-

[1] This has been reported to me by travellers and others, but
I cannot get an authoritative scientific record for the fact.

tions took place during the baby's suckling, particularly for the first eight days after its birth ; also Temesváry (*Journ. Obstet. and Gyn. Brit. Emp.*, 1903, vol. iii, p. 511) found that the natural involution of the womb after birth was distinctly more rapid in those who nursed their babies than in those who did not.

Prolonging the nursing period does undoubtedly not tend to increase the beauty of the woman's bosom but to deteriorate it, but, for at any rate the first few months, it is *very* advantageous both to the mother and to the child that she should feed it naturally. If throughout the nursing period she slings her breast properly from above, and if when the nursing period ceases she massages and treats the breast properly, it should not lose its beauty in the way which is alas, to-day, too general.

Mothers, in the self-sacrifice involved in their motherhood, too often forget their duty to remain beautiful. All youth is revolted by ugliness, consciously or unconsciously. A girl should not be indirectly taught to dread motherhood herself by seeing the wreckage her own mother has allowed it to make of her. A high demand for beauty of form by mothers is not selfishness but a racial duty.

CHAPTER XVII

Baby's Rights

" The nation that first finds a practical reconciliation between science and idealism is likely to take the front place among the peoples of the world."

DEAN INGE: *Outspoken Essays.*

BABY's rights are fundamental. They are :
To be wanted.
To be loved before birth as well as after birth.

To be given a body untainted by any heritable disease, uncontaminated by any of the racial poisons.

To be fed on the food that nature supplies, or, if that fails, the very nearest substitute that can be discovered.

To have fresh air to breathe ; to play in the sunshine with his limbs free in the air ; to crawl about on sweet clean grass.

When he is good, to do what baby wants to do and not what his parents want ; for instance, to sleep most of his time, not to sit up

and crow in response to having his cheeks pinched
or his sides tickled.

When he is naughty, to do what his parents
want and not what he wants : to be made to
understand the " law of the jungle." From his
earliest days he must be disciplined in relation
to the great physical facts of existence, to which
he will always hereafter have to bow. The
sooner he comprehends this, the better for his
future.

Most young mothers, even those who have
had the advantage of highly trained maternity
nurses to assist them at first, later require
authoritative advice about how to treat the
baby for whom they have given so much,
and to whom they wish to give every possible
advantage. Many books give advice to the
young mother and to these she may turn. I
do not wish to duplicate what they say, but
advise every one who has an infant, even if they
think they know all about the best method of
bringing it up, to possess a copy of Dr. Truby
King's *Feeding and Care of Baby* for reference.
It is the most practical, sensible and best illustrated book of its kind.

There is, therefore, on the subject of baby's
material rights not very much more that I need
to say, but there is one elementary right very
generally overlooked, and that is the right to
love in anticipation.

Baby's right to be *wanted* is an individual right which is of racial importance. No human being should be brought into the world unless his parents desire to take on the responsibility of that new life which must, for so long, be dependent upon them.

Far too many of the present inhabitants of this earth who are *not* wanted because of their inferiority, were children who came to reluctant, perhaps horror-stricken, mothers. To this fact, I trace very largely the mental and physical aberrations which are to-day so prevalent ; to this also I trace the bitterness, the unrest, the spirit of strife and malignity which seem to be without precedent in the world at present [see also *The Control of Parenthood*, final section, and, for the remedy, my book, *Wise Parenthood*, both published by Putnam].

The warped and destructive impulse of revolution which is sweeping over so many people at present must have its roots in some deep wrong.

Revolution is not a natural activity for human beings. Though the revolutionary impulse has swept through sections of humanity many times in its history, it is essentially unnatural, an indication of warping and poisoning, and a cause of further and perhaps irreparable damage.

Happy people do not indulge in revolution. Happy people with a deep sense of underlying

contentment and satisfaction in life may yet
strive ardently to improve and beautify everything round them. They strive in the same
direction as the main current of life—that is the
growth and unfolding of ever increasing beauty.
The revolutionaries—bitter, soured and profoundly unhappy—pit their strength against
the normal stream of life and destroy, break down
and rob. Too long humanity has had to endure
such outbreaks owing to its general blindness
and lack of understanding of their causes.

Until the scientific spirit of profound inquiry
into fundamental causes becomes general even
in a small section of the community, superficial
and apparently obvious explanations are accepted to account for results which really arise
from profound and secret springs.

The " divine discontent " which has impelled
humanity forward along the path of constructive
progress is a very different thing from the bitter
discontent which leads to revolutionary and
destructive outbursts. The village blacksmith of
the well-known song, using his healthy muscles
on hard, useful work which gives him a deep
physical satisfaction, may feel the former and help
forward the stream of progress in his village.

The aim of reformers to-day should be to
provide for every one neither ease nor comfort,
nor high wages nor short hours, but the deeper
necessities of a full and contented life, bodies

able to respond with satisfaction to the strain of hard work performed under conditions which satisfy the mind in the most fundamental way of all—the deep, sub-conscious satisfaction which is given by the sweet smell of earth, by fresh air and sunshine, and green things around one.

We draw from all these things some subtle ingredient without which our natures are weakened so that a further strain sends them awry. To-day we are so deeply involved with the hydra-headed monster of the revolutionary spirit that there does not seem time to deal with it radically, to attempt to understand it, and consequently to conquer it for ever. Even now, when for the first time humanity is on a large scale beginning to tackle fundamental problems, I have seen no indication that the source of revolution is being sought for in the right place.

What is the source of revolution ?

The revolutionaries through the ages, feeling themselves jar with their surroundings, have been ensnared by the nearest obvious things, the happier surrounding of others. These they have endeavoured to snatch at and destroy, thinking thereby to improve their own and their comrades' lot. Their deductions, though profoundly false, have appeared even obviously right to many.

External grievances are what the revolutionary is out to avenge : external benefits are what he is out to gain. Generally this is expressed in terms of higher wages, a share, or all, of the capital of those supposed to be better off, or the material possessions of others. These are the things that nearly all strikers and revolutionaries are upsetting the world to get, thinking —perhaps sincerely—that these things will give them the happiness for which, consciously or unconsciously, they yearn. The truth is, however, that it is a much more intimate thing than money or possessions which they need. They need new bodies and new hearts.

Most of the revolutionaries I have met are people who have been warped or stunted in their own personal growth. One sees upon their minds or bodies the marks and scars of dwarfing, stunting or lack of balance. They have known wretchedness both in themselves and in their families far more intimate and penetrating than that of mere poverty.

That, they may answer, is an external grievance which has been imposed upon them by society. In effect they say : " Society has starved us, given us bad conditions." Thus they foster a grievance against " society " in their minds. One bitter leader said to me :—

I was one of fourteen children, and my mother had only a little three-roomed cottage near Glasgow. We nearly starved when I was young. I know what the poor suffer at the hands of society.

But it was not society that put fourteen children into that cottage ; it was the mother herself. Her own ignorance, helpless ignorance perhaps, was the source of her children's misery. The most for which society can be blamed concerning that family is in tolerating such a plague-spot of ignorance in its midst. Nor is this pestilential ignorance by any means only confined to the financially poor.

This country, and nearly all the world, has innumerable homes in which the seed of revolution is sown in myriads of minds from the moment they are conceived. Revolted, horror-stricken mothers bear children whose coming birth they fear.

A starved, stunted outlook is stamped upon their brains and bodies in the most intimate manner before they come into the world, so oriented towards it that they *must* run counter to the healthy, happy constructive stream of human life.

What wonder at the rotten conditions of our population when these are common experiences of the mothers of our race :—

For fifteen years I was in a very poor state of health owing to continual pregnancy. As soon as I was over one trouble it was started all over again.[1]

---

[1] I refer the reader to that poignant book, *Maternity, Letters from Working Women*, collected by the Women's Co-operative Guild. Bell, 1915.

Again :—

> During pregnancy I suffered much. When at the end of ten years I determined that this state of things should not go on any longer.

Again :—

> My grandmother had twenty children. Only eight lived to about fourteen years; only two to a good old age.

Again :—

> I cannot tell you all my sufferings during the time of motherhood. I thought, like hundreds of women to-day, that it was only natural, and that you had to bear it. I had three children and one miscarriage in three years.

Need I go on?

There lies the real root of revolution.

The secret revolt and bitterness which permeates every fibre of the unwillingly pregnant and suffering mothers has been finding its expression in the lives and deeds of their children. We have been breeding revolutionaries through the ages and at an increasing rate since the crowding into cities began, and women were forced to bear children beyond their strength and desires in increasingly unnatural conditions.

Also since women have heard rumours that

such enslaved motherhood is not necessary,
that the wise know a way of keeping their
motherhood voluntary, the revolt in the mother
has become conscious with consequent injury
to the child.

Increasingly, the first of baby's rights is to be
wanted.

Concerning baby's right to be fed on the food
that nature supplies, or if that fails on the very
nearest substitute that can be discovered, there
are to-day so many who urge that an infant
shall be fed by its own mother, that it is perhaps
needless to repeat arguments so impressive.
Nevertheless, perhaps it is as well to remind
young mothers of two or three of the most
vital facts. The first is that no artificial substitute, however perfectly prepared and chemically
analysed, can possibly give those very subtle
constituents which are found in the mother's
own milk and which vary from individual to
individual. These probably are in the nature
of the vitamines now so well known in fresh
food, but they are something more specifically
individual than can be scientifically detected.
The fresh milk of its own mother has a peculiar
value to the child which is greater than that
of any foster mother.

For this reason alone, were it the only one,
every young mother should nurse her own
baby if possible ; but, on the other hand, to-day

it not infrequently happens that the mother may have an apparent flow of milk, quite sufficient for the infant in quantity, but that milk may be devoid of the necessary supply of fat or sugars or some other ingredient for complete nutriment. When this is so, it is often wisest to allow the mother to nurse the child partly and to supplement its diet by other milk.

Various schools of doctors and maternity nurses have differed even on this matter, but it is quite obvious that if the actual food value of the mother's milk is below a certain point then the added value of its individual vitamine-like qualities will not wholly compensate for the loss of actual nourishment.

Among baby's rights, I should perhaps also make it clear that there is his right that he should not be used as a bulwark between his mother and another baby in a way which is sometimes recommended so that a mother may go on nursing her infant for a very long time, sometimes even into its second year, in the hope that this nursing may prevent her conceiving again. Such a course of action is very harmful both to the child and to her and should never be followed. Such a practice is, of course, much less common in this country (except among aliens) than it is abroad where I have seen healthy children of even three or four years of age nursing upon their mother's knees.

In these days, perhaps it is hardly necessary to accentuate baby's other rights since the century of the child dawned a generation ago. To-day it is perhaps almost more important to accentuate the rights of others who exist in the neighbourhood of a baby. But on the other hand if one looks penetratingly at the whole problem of character development, one sees that among baby's rights is its right to be trained from the very first so that its life shall be as little hindered by friction as may be possible: that it should be taught the elementary rules of conduct and necessary conformity with the hard material facts of existence from the very first. A wise nurse's or mother's training from the earliest weeks of infancy may make or mar a future man's or woman's chance of getting on in the world and making a success of their lives, by making or marring the character, the capacity to obey, the formation of regular and hygienic habits and the realization of the physical facts of the world.

The ancient Greeks taught their youth to reverence that which was beneath them, that which was around them, and that which was above them. In my opinion this right of youth to be placed in its proper orientation in relation to the world has been neglected of late. We are suffering from the wayward revolt from an earlier and perhaps harsher type of mistake, that of too greatly controlling and thwarting the child's impulses. We must maintain a just balance and return to the due mean in which the right of a child, not only to be well born but well trained, is universally recognized.

CHAPTER XVIII

The Weakest Link in the Human Chain

" This shall be thy reward—that the ideal shall be real to thee."

OLIVE SCHREINER: *Dreams.*

PROVERBS innumerable and daily experience have familiarized every one with the idea that the citizen is moulded and his or her essential characteristics determined in childhood, and as a result of childhood's training. The most profoundly operative of all his qualities is his potential sex attitude, because it is that which determines his experience of sex and marriage, which colours his thoughts towards women throughout his life, which inclines his mind nobly towards his own racial actions or which leaves him weak and frivolous in his attitude towards the greatest profundities of life.

Children, otherwise brought up with every care and forethought, surrounded by all that

love and money can give them, are too generally
left, without their mother's guidance or their
father's wisdom, to discover the great facts of
life partly by instinct and partly from the vulgar
talk of servants or soiled children a little older
than themselves. Worse even than this takes
place, because most generally in this connection
they not only do not hear the truth from their
mother's lips, but they learn from her their
most influential and earliest lesson in lying.

The curious thing about the particularly
pernicious form of lying which deals with racial
things in the presence of childhood is that we
have the habit of thinking it quite innocent.
Indeed we have even acquired the habit of thinking it one of the charming form of lies ; hence
when we are in a reforming mood, seeking for
the origins of the wrongs we are trying to put
right, we pass these " charming " lies by, thinking them harmless.

Where did each one of us first learn to lie ?
*Nearly every one who is now grown up got his
(or her) first lesson in lying at his mother's knee.*
To the little child, in his narrow but ever widening world, the mother is the supreme ruler,
the all-wise provider of food, clothes, pleasures
and pains. The mother (the child instinctively
feels) must be also the source of wisdom.

Question after question about himself and
his surroundings springs up in the baby mind.

Mother is asked them all, and for every one she has some sort of an answer. Then inevitably, at three or four, or five years old comes the question :—" Mother, where did you find me ? "—" Mother, how was I born ? "

Then comes the lie.

The child is told about the doctor bringing him in a bag—or a stork flying in through the window—or the accidental finding under the gooseberry bush.

All children delight in fairy tales, but instinctively they know very well the difference between a fairy tale which is recounted to them as a story in answer to their mood of " make-believe " and a fiction which is putting them off when they are seeking the truth.

If the mother who feels herself too ignorant or too self-conscious to answer the truth to the child's questions takes him on her knee and deliberately tells him in a " make-believe " mood a fairy tale, the child will then not feel that the mother has lied. *He will feel, however, that he must ask some one else for the truth.*

But most mothers give the answer containing the fiction of the gooseberry bush, or whatever it may be, in a manner indicating that that is what the child must believe, and the child receives the information as a serious answer to his serious question. It is then a lie, and a pernicious lie.

Racial knowledge, instinct, whatever you like to call it, is subtler and stronger in baby minds than we dulled grown-ups are inclined to think. The youngest child has a half-consciousness that what its mother said in answer to this question was not true.

Nurse, or auntie, a friend's governess, or any one else who seems wise and powerful, is asked the same question when mother is not there, and the chances are that if mother had given the stork version auntie gives the gooseberry bush or some other fiction which she particularly favours.

The baby ponders intermittently, inconsequently, perhaps at long intervals, perhaps after years, but ultimately it realizes that its mother lied to it.

In this way infinite injury has been done to the whole human stock, and more particularly women have suffered from the dishonesty and the inherent incapacity of our society to be frank and truthful about the most profound and the most terrible aspects of sex, namely, its diseases. A wife or a mother has the right to be told the truth.

Women, and particularly mothers, have been outrageously wronged by the deliberate lies and untruthful atmosphere about the greater problems of sex in which the learned have enshrouded them : but mothers have themselves

given the first bent to the little sprouting twig
of that tree of knowledge, and they have bent
it *away* from the sunlight of truth and clean
and happy understanding.

The mother's excuse is, or would be if she
felt herself in any way to blame (which, by the
way, deplorably, she very seldom does) that
these terrible mysteries of origin are not suitable
for the little innocent child to ponder over.
She thinks they would shock him. But here
the mother is profoundly mistaken.

*The age of innocence is the age when all know-
ledge is pure.* At three, four, or five years old,
everything is taken for granted—everything in
the universe is equally a surprise, and is at the
same time accepted without question as being
in the natural course of events. If true answers
were given to the tiny child's questions, they
would seem quite rational—not in the least
more surprising than the fact that oak trees
grow from acorns, or that the cook gets a jam
tart out of a hot oven.

All the world's events seem magic at that
age, and if no exceptional mystery were made
of the magic of his own advent, the child would
feel it as natural as all the rest, and having
asked the question and obtained satisfactory,
simple unaccentuated answers, would let his
little mind run on to the thousand other questions he wants to ask. The essential racial

knowledge would slip naturally and sweetly into his mind mingled with a myriad other new impressions.

There is no self-consciousness, no personal shamefacedness, about a tiny child. It accepts the great truths of the universe in the grand manner.

If the mother has never failed her child, has always given it what she could of wisdom, she will retain his trust and his confidence. When he gets a little older she can teach him to go to no one else for talk about the intimacies of life, which the child is quick to realize are not discussed openly amongst strangers.

Then, later on, when personal consciousness and shyness begin, there need not be the acute constraint and tension of the shame-faced elder speaking to a mind awakening to itself. Deep in the child's consciousness, deeper even than its conscious memory goes, the true big facts are planted.

To tell a child of twelve or fourteen the truth is, for most parents, an impossibly difficult matter. The reason for this is that it is then too late for essentials ; only details are then suitable or necessary.

Little children spend much of their early time in exploring themselves and their immediate surroundings—all is mysterious, all at first unknown. Their own feet and hands, their powers of locomotion and of throwing some object to a distance, the curls of their own hair, the pain they encounter in their bodies when explorations bring them in contact with sharp angles : all are equally mysterious, together forming a wonder-world. And babies are very young indeed when they explore with all the rest of their bodies, the rudiments of those of their racial organs with which they can acquaint themselves. *In my opinion, the attitude of a man or woman through life is largely determined by the attitude adopted by the mother towards the racial organs* BEFORE *the child was old enough consciously to remember any instruction that was imparted.*

Advice is often given in these more enlightened days to instruct your boy or girl in his racial power or duties when he or she is ten or twelve years old. This to many seems very young, and they hesitate and defer it till they are older and " can understand better." In my opinion, this is already eight or ten years too late.

The child's first instruction in its attitude towards its sex organs, its first account of the generation of human beings, should be given when it is two or three years old ; given with other instruction, of which it is still too young to comprehend more than part, but which it is nevertheless old enough to comprehend in part. Very simple instruction given reverently at suitable opportunities at that early age will impress itself upon

the very *texture* of the child's mind, before the
time of actual memories, so that from the very
first possible beginnings its tendencies are in
the direction of truth and reverent understanding.

*A child so tiny will usually not remember one
word of what was said to it, but the effects on his
outlook will be deep.*   For at that early age, children are meditatively absorbing and being impressed by the psychological states and feelings
of their instructors and companions, and if, in
these very earliest months, the mother or
guardian makes the mistake of treating ribaldly
the tiny organs or of speaking lightly in the
child's presence, or of directly lying to the child
about these facts, that child receives a mental
warp and injury which nothing can ever eradicate
entirely, which may in later years through
bitter and befouling experiences be lived down
as an old scar that has healed, but which will
have permanently injured it.

I hold this to be a profound truth, and one
which it is urgent that humanity should realize.
I trust that my view will establish itself on every
hand. If that were my way, I could easily
write a whole volume on this theme, and coin
a polysyllabic terminology in which to mould
and harden thought on the subject. But I
prefer that a few simple words should slip like
vital seed into the hearts of mothers, and that
they may mould the race.

It is ignorance of this truth which has led to the dishonouring and befouling of pure and beautiful youth, which is the original source of the greater part of all the social troubles and the sex difficulties of adolescence.

The tiny child of two or three years old, just beginning to perceive and piece together the psychological impressions stamped upon it by its environment and the mind-states of those around it, is the weakest link in the chain of our social consciousness. Physically, the new born babe for the first few days of its life is the weakest link in the chain, the most liable physically to extinction, but spiritually, socially the link most liable to warping, even destruction, is the awakening mind, the still half-sleeping consciousness, of the child between two and three years old.

The mother or guardian then who desires her son or daughter to face the great facts of life beautifully and profoundly should begin from the first to mould that attitude in the child It may appear to the unthinking like building castles in the sand even to hint at truths which it cannot comprehend to a child who remembers nothing of the words used in later years. This is not so. What the child absorbs is less the actual words than the tone of voice, the mode of expression that spiritually impresses itself upon its own little soul.

Then there comes a later stage for most

civilized human beings, usually after they are
three years old, when there arises the possibility of permanent consciousness through permanent and specific memory of things seen,
done or heard. Most grown-ups of the present
generation will have some vivid memory, dating
back to when they were between three and four
years old, when they received a strong mental
impression that grown-ups were lying to them
or that there was something funny or silly in
questions which they asked. Perhaps they
noticed that whilst Jack the Giant Killer was
taken seriously, questions about where pussy got
her kittens were laughed at. Almost each one
of us who is to-day grown up then received some
grievous injury. This time is of great importance in the psychology not only of the child,
but of the whole adult race arising from the
growing up of each child, for one's earliest
memories are few but very vivid. As things
are to-day, generally between the ages of three
and four or so, in the months which are likely
to yield a lifelong memory, the spirit is wounded
by the shock of a serious lie.

When as a mother or father you are with
your children it is vital to be most careful to
answer truly, and if possible beautifully, the
questions which arise. No one can foresee
which question and answer may make that
terrible impression which lasts for a lifetime.

When your little son or daughter is about the age of three or four or five, the day will come when you are asked questions about the most fundamental facts in human life, and then the answers to these questions contain the probability of a lifelong memory.   Answer with the *truth*.

Many parents are anxious to tell their children the great truths in a wise and beautiful manner. But few feel that they know how to do it, for it is a most difficult thing to know how to answer searching questions about profound subjects, and particularly about those which the community wrongly considers shameful. Each mother knows, or should know, the temperament and needs of her child, so that the adaptation of the advice I give should be varied to suit the individual child. In essence, however, children's demands at an early age are remarkably similar, and the questions of children on birth and sex differ in form, though seldom in substance.

The following conversation between a mother and her little son indicates what seems to me the best way first to tell a child who has reached the age when he may have lasting memory of the facts that he is blindly seeking in his baby questions. It will not suffice to learn the answers off by heart ; the baby will then soon confound his elders, but the substance of the conversation should prove useful.

14

The very first time the query comes : " Mother where did you get me ? " the mother must not divert the child's interest, or hesitate, but should be ready at once to answer :—

" God and Daddy and I together made you, because we wanted you.[1] "

" Did God help ? Couldn't He do it all Himself ? "

" You know when you and I are playing with bricks together, you like Mummy to help, but not to do it all. God thought Daddy and Mummy would like Him to help, but not to do everything, because Daddy and Mummy enjoyed making you much more than you enjoy playing with bricks."

That may suffice for the time, because little children are very readily satisfied with one or two facts about any one subject, and the talk could easily be diverted. The little mind may brood over what was told, and some time later —perhaps a few days, perhaps even a few months or more—this question will come up again, possibly in a different form:—

" Mummy, when was I born ? "

The mother should give the day and say :—

" You know your birthday comes every year on the 18th of April. That birthday is what reminds us of the day you were born, and each birthday you are a whole year older."

---

[1] At the request of many readers this conversation was published in the *Sunday Chronicle.*

" I'm five now."

" Yes, so you were born five years ago on your birthday."

" Where was I before I was born ? "

" Don't you remember I told you that God and Daddy and I made you ? "

" Yes . . . Did you make me on my birthday ? "

" Not all in one day; you took much longer to make than that."

" How long did I take to make ? "

" A long, long time. Little children are so precious they cannot be made in a hurry."

" How long did I take ? "

" Nearly a year—nine whole months."

" Did baby take as long ? "

" Yes, just the same time. Baby is just as precious as you are."

" I'm bigger."

" Now you are, but you were baby's size when you were baby's age. You are bigger because you have grown since your first birthday."

Again the subject may perhaps drop, or it may be carried directly forward.

" What is being born ? "

" Being born is being shown to the world and seeing the world for the first time. At the end of nine months after God and Daddy and Mummy started to make you, you were ready to open your eyes and breathe and cry, and be a real live baby, and that day they showed you to somebody and you saw the world. That was being born."

" Where was I before you finished making me ? "

" Mummy kept you hidden away so that nobody at all should see you."

" *Where* was I hidden ? "

" You were hidden in a most wonderful place, in the place where only quite little babies can be while God and their mummies are making them."

" Show me; I want to go back there."

" You can never go back; it is only while you are being made you can be there. After your first birthday, you can never go back."

" Where was I ? "

" Well, you know, little babies that are being made are very, very delicate, and they have to be kept very warm and comfortable, and nobody must see them, and they must be close, close up to their mummies."

The child may interject, " And their daddies too ? "

" Yes, if they have got loving daddies, the daddy keeps close to the mummy; but while babies are being made it is God and mummy that have most of the work to do. That is why you must always love your mummies and obey them."

The child may be temporarily satisfied, or may continue at once:—

" But where *was* it that I was while you were making me ? "

" What is the warmest, softest, safest place you can think of ? Mummy's heart: that is all warm with love. The place Mummy hid you while God and she were making you was right underneath her heart."

" Her real heart—the heart that beats like a clock ticking ? "

" Yes, her real heart, just here."

The mother should lay the child's hand on her heart and let him feel it beating.

"And just inside, right underneath here, Mummy kep*
you while God was helping her to make you."

The child who has been brought up in a home
of love and tenderness and beauty will find this
a thrilling and beautiful thought, like a little
boy whom I know personally, and to whom
this fact was told in this way. Solemnly, and
without a word, he went away from his mother
into the middle of the room and stood deep in
thought for several minutes. Then he turned,
looked round, and rushed across the room,
threw himself into his mother's lap, his arms
round her neck and cried : "Oh, Mummy,
Mummy, then I was right inside you."

For days afterwards he was filled with a
rapturous joy, and at times used to leave his
play and come to his mother and put his arms
round her neck, saying : "Oh, Mummy, that
is why I love you so."

Whatever form the child's feeling may take,
the opportunity should not be allowed to pass
without a little addition to the conversation,
and the mother should say :—

"And you see that is why you must never talk to any one
but Daddy and Mummy, or God through your prayers, about
such things. As God and Daddy and Mummy, and no one
else made your little body, so every thing you want to know
about it, all the questions you want to ask, you should ask of
them and no one else. You see, you are different from any

other child in the world, and as Daddy and Mummy helped to make you, only they know your works. So whatever it is you want to know, or whatever it is that goes wrong, it is Mummy and Daddy who can tell you about it."

Once may be sufficient for a child to be told the greater truths it desires to know, but it is seldom that the child will leave so wonderful a subject entirely alone after first learning of it, and many portions of the beautiful facts will have to be repeated in a variety of forms, or in just the same words, as are repeated again and again the beloved fairy tales. The child, however, will be quick to know the difference between this story and fairy tales, for children have an instinct for truth at a much earlier age than grown-ups generally remember.

A further series of questions will probably arise when the child is about twelve.

The essential difficulties of these later questions, and the shamefaced self-consciousness so usual between parent and child will never arise if from the first the deep truths have been known to the child.

The child so instructed is not supplied with all necessary facts, and instruction of a more specific and exact nature will have to be repeated at further intervals throughout its life, but on this foundation, further knowledge can be built without having to wipe out anything already implanted, without having to contradict earlier instruction, or to acknowledge the gravest error of having lied. Life teaches much to a quick child trained to observation, particularly in the country, where all children should spend much of their time. If the little one has been told what has been given in the previous pages it will have all the essential truths on to which it will fit in for itself the other data which daily life will bring it ; thus it may garner a harvest of facts one by one.

Concerning the later instruction which will be necessary, the information can be given in many ways. Some advocate school instruction of children of twelve or more in the physiology of all the members of the body, so that the racial powers are treated in their proper place in conjunction with the digestive organs, brain, lungs, etc. Some parents prefer to give the instruction themselves, for none but they can know so well the individual needs of the child.

Much has already been written and is available in the voluminous literature about the presentation of the facts to be imparted at the various later ages, and almost every book advises comparisons with flowers. For the later ages of ten years and after, this is probably the best introduction for specific details, but for the first and earliest instruction of the baby mind, such direct simple answers as I have indicated are, I am sure, the best.

Children whose parents have treated them as I advise in this chapter are *essentially safe* whatever form later instruction may take. They will then have the vitality to survive lies, although ever to lie to them will be putting a cruel and useless strain on their recuperative powers. If the little child is started upon its life with a beautiful and true conception of its relation to its mother, and of man's relation to woman, it will be unlikely indeed that it will grow up a hooligan who flouts his parents or a loose and lascivious destroyer of women.

CHAPTER XIX

The Cost of Coffins

He only is free who can control himself.

EPICTETUS.

The imposition of motherhood upon a married woman in absolute despite of her health and of the interests of the children is none the less an iniquity because it has at present the approval of Church and State.

SALEEBY: Woman and Womanhood.

WHY do poor slum mothers buy more coffins than do the same number of rich women?

The incredulous may answer this question by asserting that they don't, but as a matter of fact they do. The Registrar-General's Report for 1911 shows that of every thousand births in the upper and middle classes, 76·4 babies die, while of a thousand births in the homes of unskilled workmen (this would be the class of the " poor " mothers) 152·5 babies die.

So that it is clear that if each member of this poorest class of mothers had exactly the same number of babies as each mother of the rich class, she would have to purchase about two coffins for every coffin bought by those whose babies are not so prone to die.

There is, however, another fact which completes the proof of my first sentence. The upper and middle classes do not have so many children per family as do the poorest class. To a thousand married people in the upper and middle classes there were born in 1911 119 babies, but to the poor mothers—the wives of the unskilled workmen—there were born 213. So that in addition to buying twice as many coffins per thousand children born, these poor mothers have nearly twice as many coffins again, owing to the fact that nearly twice as many children are born to them.

I wonder if poor women have ever asked themselves if they can afford coffins at this rate ?

Of course the coffins of these poor little babies are very small, and do not require very much wood to make them. But let us think in what other ways they cost : To the mother they cost not only all the little the baby had eaten, and used in the way of clothes before its death, but all the wastage of her own vitality while she was bearing it ; she could not work so well, at any rate towards the end of the time.

Home duties had to be somewhat neglected; the older children had to go to school dirtier and less cared for ; the husband had less comfort and fewer smiles ; every one in the family was poorer, not only in material things and in the work that might make material things, but in happiness and buoyancy.

It needs no imagination to realize, when you have once grasped these facts, that poor people are much less able to spare the cost of a doomed baby than are the better class people. Then why do they so often indulge in this tragic luxury ? Chiefly through lack of knowledge, through ignorance, particularly on the part of the mother.

Often ignorance is blind and unaware that it is ignorance, stupidly blundering through life ; but this is not always the mother's attitude. She may, indeed she often does, passionately desire knowledge and seek for it wherever she thinks she may find it in her restricted circle. Too tragically often she is baffled in her search.

Some years before the war, when I was lecturing at a Northern University, a little incident opened my eyes to this fact. I was young and had not encountered this aspect of life before, and it burnt itself into my consciousness as one of the most vivid impressions of my life. It was this :—

One of my students was a woman who was

hoping to qualify as a medical doctor, and she was having tea with me and chatting about the events of the day. As part of her training she had been assisting the doctor in dealing with out-patients at a hospital, and a woman had brought in a miserable little baby, which wailed all the time and which the mother explained wouldn't put on any flesh or grow into a nice, healthy baby whatever she did with it.

The mother, with tears in her eyes, made an intensely earnest appeal to the doctor to tell her what was to her unaccountably wrong with the infant.

She was a fine strapping woman, and thought her babies ought to be large and healthy. She said this was her third or fourth, and the others had all died when they were very little.

This happened more than seven years ago. Thank God our racial attitude has changed since then.

The doctor put her off with some soothing platitudes, but the woman driven to despair said : " I believe there's something wrong with my man. If there's something wrong with my man I won't have babies no more—it's just cruel to see them miserable like this and have them dying one after the other. Won't you, for God's sake, tell me whether there's anything wrong with my man or not ? " This appeal was met by the assurance that there was nothing wrong, and she should go on having babies and do her duty by her husband.

My medical woman student said that it was glaringly obvious that the baby was syphilitic.

I asked her why she did not immediately tell the mother the truth. She shrugged her shoulders and said : " I've got my exam. to pass ; if I did a thing like that Dr. —— would stop me going to the hospital. I can't afford to take risks like that. Why, he might not only stop me, but it would do the other women students a lot of harm too."

This was before the war, and England was less enlightened, less eager for medical women's assistance than the war has made her, and it was then a fight for a girl to get a footing in the hospitals for the wide experience she needed for a general practice.

I vowed to myself that I would never forget that mother, and that some day I would batter at the brazen gates of knowledge on her behalf.

Here was a mother with a glimmering of the truth, seeking passionately for knowledge from the one person she had a right to turn to for this knowledge, and she was put off with lies, encouraged again to bear the cost of a hopelessly doomed birth ; to risk the agonies of child-birth, to bring into the world a creature who for a short spell would be tormented and then would cost her a coffin.

By refusing his scientific advice, that doctor in reality sent that woman, whose desire to know was stirred, to the gossip of the slum alley and the street corner. There she would get a blurred and inaccurate, if not actually harmful, idea of what he should have been able to tell her in a clean, simple language based on scientific fact.

When this is put down on paper, I feel as though it would be ridiculous to begin to point out the monstrous cruelty and the monstrous folly of such an action as that doctor's. Yet such action was not isolated, it did not depend on one man's warped conceptions of loyalty to another unknown man, " the husband." Since the war a public realization of the racial destructiveness of such diseases has been increased and the woman and her husband would to-day be more likely to receive medical treatment.

But even to-day if a mother is truly told that there is " something wrong with her man," would she also certainly be told how in wise and healthy fashion she can herself supplement what his criminal negligence neglected? If a husband is careless and callous a woman must save herself and the community from the waste and the misery of irretrievably doomed births.

She will indeed be an exceptionally lucky woman if she to-day finds in public hos-

pitals doctors to whom she could turn for knowledge how *best* to control conception, though
such knowledge is not only essential to her
private well-being, but essential to her in the
fulfilment of her duties as a citizen.

This little incident is but one illustration
of many aspects of the subject. It is not only
disease which necessitates restraint on parenthood.
No healthy woman can bear a long series of
infants in rapid succession without loss both
to them and to herself. This is discussed in
my *Wise Parenthood*.

Any one who thinks will see clearly that no
civilized country, not even the richest in the
world, can afford babies' coffins. Though they
are smaller than grown-up people's they are
more costly, for they are waste and nothing
but waste. A grown-up individual, man or
woman, has, we hope at any rate, given some
return to the community in work or in ideas
for all that his life has cost. But the infant's
death is sheer unmitigated waste.

If all the mothers who realize this and who
feel their need for the best help that science
can give them, would insist and persist in their
enquiries for a knowledge of the most reliable
results of modern science, they would in the
end succeed in getting them. There is enough
knowledge now in the world for the race to
transform itself in a couple of generations.

CHAPTER XX

The Creation of a New and Irradiated Race

Ah, Love! could thou and I with fate conspire
To grasp this sorry Scheme of Things entire,
Would not we shatter it to bits—and then
Remould it nearer to the Heart's desire.

OMAR KHAYYAM.

ON parents' love for the helpless child depends the existence of our race. Human parenthood necessitates not only the desire for offspring, but the willing care of them during the long years while they are helpless and dependent. Were this desire and willingness not deeply implanted in us our race would become extinct, as in some strange way, the higher type of ancient Greeks vanished from the world.

Not only throughout the lower creatures do we find the responsibilities of parenthood increasing as we go up the scale towards the higher, but, even in the various grades of highly civilized man, the responsibility for the children is ever greater in proportion with the general culture and position of the parents.

Not many years ago the labourer's child could be set to work early and could very shortly earn his keep ; while at the same time the young gentleman was an expense and care to his father and mother until he had passed through the University of Oxford or Cambridge, and amongst some even until he had made his "finishing" world tour. The trend of legislation has continuously extended the age of irresponsible youth in the lower and lower middle classes, until it now approaches that of the middle and upper class youth. A stride in this direction was taken by the last Education Act, which has made education compulsory throughout the whole country to an age which is nearly university age.

I need not labour the resulting effect of the ever increasing prolongation of youth. It is not only apparent but has received sufficient treatment from the hands of various authors and thinkers.

Its corollary, however, has still not received that clear and direct thought which its significance demands. Parenthood under the present *régime*, is not only an increasing responsibility and expense, it has become so great a strain upon the resources of those who have for them-

15

selves and their children a high standard of living that it is tending to become a rare privilege for some who would otherwise gladly propagate large families.

As Dean Inge reminded us (*Outspoken Essays*, 1919), there was a stage in the high civilization of Greece when slaves were only allowed to rear a child as a reward for their good behaviour. I find a curious parallel to this in the treatment of a section of our society by our present community.

Crushed by the burden of taxation which they have not the resources to meet and to provide for children also : crushed by the national cost of the too numerous children of those who do not contribute to the public funds by taxation, yet who recklessly bring forth from an inferior stock individuals who are not self-supporting, the middle and superior artisan classes have, without perceiving it, come almost to take the position of that ancient slave population. It is only as a reward for their thrift and foresight, for their care and self-denial that they find themselves able (that is allowed by financial circumstances) to have one or perhaps two children. Hence by a strange parallel working of divers forces, the best, the thriftiest, the most serious-minded, the most desiring of parenthood are to-day those who are forced by circumstances into the position of the ancient slave and allowed to rear but one or two children as a result perhaps of a lifetime of valuable service and of loving union with a wife well fitted to bear more offspring. While on the other hand, society allows the diseased, the racially negligent, the thriftless, the careless, the feeble-minded, the very lowest and worst members of the community, to produce innumerable tens of thousands of stunted, warped, and inferior infants. If they live, a large proportion of these are doomed from their very physical inheritance to be at the best but partly self-supporting, and thus to drain the resources of those classes above them which have a sense of responsibility. The better classes, freed from the cost of the institutions, hospitals, prisons and so on, principally filled by the inferior stock, would be able to afford to enlarge their own families, and at the same time not only to save misery but to multiply a hundredfold the contribution in human life-value to the riches of the State.

The immensity of the power of parenthood, both on the personal lives which it brings into existence, and on the community of which each individual is to form a part, is not yet perceived by our Statesmen in its true perspective.

The power of parenthood ought no longer to be exercised by *all*, however inferior, as an "individual right." It is profoundly a duty and a privilege, and it is essentially the concern of the whole community. It should be the policy of the community to encourage in every way the parenthood of those whose circumstances and conditions are such that there is a reasonable anticipation that they will give rise to healthy, well-endowed future citizens. It should be the policy of the community to discourage from parenthood all whose circumstances are such as would make probable the introduction of weakened, diseased or debased future citizens. It is the urgent duty of the community to make parenthood impossible for those whose mental and physical conditions are such that there is well-nigh a certainty that their offspring must be physically and mentally tainted, if not utterly permeated by disease. That the community should allow syphilitic parents to bring forth a sequence of blind syphilitic infants is a state of affairs so monstrous that it would be hardly credible were it not a fact.

Parenthood, with the divine gift of love in its power, with the glorious potentialities of handing on a radiant, wholesome, beautiful youth should be a sacred and preserved gift, a privilege only to be exercised by those who rationally comprehend the counter-balancing duties. But so long as parenthood is kept outside the realm of rational thought and reasoned action, so long will we as a race slide at an ever-increasing speed towards the utter deterioration of our stock through the reckless increase of the debased, which is necessarily counterbalanced by the unnatural limiting of the families of the more educated and responsible, whose sense of duty to the unborn forbids them to bring into the world children whom they cannot educate and environ at least as well as they themselves were reared.

In earlier generations the child was taught to speak of its parents in a respectful and grateful tone as the " august authors of its being," but this right and proper instruction in reverence was coupled with an arbitrary disposal of the child, and a certain harshness in its training against which the later generations have revolted. As is usual the reformers have deviated from rectitude in the opposite direction, so that to-day to find children with deep respect for their parents is uncommon. Reverence is being exacted by some rather from the parent towards the child as a fresh, new and unspoilt being. This too often results in spoiling the child, which is an equally foolish and hampering proceeding. The child should be taught from its earliest days profound respect, reverence and gratitude towards its parents, and in particular towards its mother, for of her very life she gave it the incomparable gift of life. True parents give the child the best and freshest and most beautiful

impulses of their lives, and, at the cost of bodily
anguish the mother bears it, and its parents
for long years nurture it, sacrificing many enjoyments which they might have but for the cost
and care of rearing it. This should be realized
by the child, who then cannot but feel gratitude
to and reverence for the authors of its being.

The sheer beauty of the world, were there no
other gain from living, is so great that the gift
of eyes and a mind to perceive it should place
the recipient of that gift for ever in a reverential
debt towards the pair who gave.

But the value of the beauty of life, and a just
appreciation of the immense gift which parenthood confers cannot be realized by all. To-day
alas, millions are born into circumstances so
wretched that life can scarcely involve a perception of beauty, or a probability of moral
action and social service. Also many myriads
of children are born of parents to whom they
can feel that they owe nothing, because they
know or inwardly perceive that they were not
desired, that they were not profoundly and
nobly loved throughout their coming, that they
were hurled into this existence through accident,
self-indulgence or stupidity. Yet parenthood
which grants life even on these terms is a
wonderful power, a cruel and relentless force
perverted from its divine possibilities.

Youth tends ever to right itself if it but

escape the taint of the profound racial diseases, and the gift of a well-conditioned body is the creation of an incomparable set of co-ordinated powers in a world in which the potentialities for the use of those powers is magical.

Innumerable are the efforts at present being made by countless different societies, official bodies and individual reformers to diminish the ever increasing ill-health and deterioration of our race, but their efforts are a fight on the losing side unless the fundamental and hitherto uncontrollable factors which make for health are there.

Doctors may cure every disease known to humanity, but while they are so doing, fresh diseases, further modifications of destructive germs, may spring into existence, the possibility of which has recently been demonstrated by French scientists who have experimented on the rapid changes which may be induced in "germs."

Prisons and reformatories, municipal milk, the feeding of school children, improvement in housing, reform of our marriage laws, schools for mothers, even schools for fathers, garden cities—not all these useful and necessary things together and many more added to them will ever touch the really profound sources of our race, will ever cause freedom from degeneracy and ill-health, will ever create that fine, glorious and beautiful race of men and women which hovers in the dreams of our reformers. Is then this dream out of reach and impossible ; are then all our efforts wasted ? No, the dream is not impossible of fulfilment; but, at present, our efforts are almost entirely wasted because *they are built upon the shifting sand and not upon the steady rock.*

The reform, *the one central reform,* which will make all the others of avail and make their work successful *is the endowing of motherhood, not with money but with the knowledge of her own power.*

For the power of a mother, consciously exerted in the voluntary procreation and joyous bearing of her children is the greatest power in the world. It is through its conscious and deliberate exercise, and through that alone, that the race may step from its present entanglements on to a higher plane, where bodies will be not only a delight to their possessors, but efficient tools in the service of the souls which temporarily inhabit them.

I maintain that this wonderful rejuvenescence and reform of the race need not be a dim and distant dream of the future. It is hovering so close at hand that it is actually within reach of those who to-day are in their young maturity ; we, at present in the flesh may link hands with grandchildren belonging to a generation so

wonderful, so endowed, and so improved out of
recognition that the miseries and the depravity
of human nature, to-day so wide-spread, may
appear like a black and hideous memory of the
past, as incredible to them as the habits of
cannibals are to us.

An ideal too distant, too remote, may interest
the dreamer and the reformer possibly, but it
cannot inspire a whole nation. An ideal within
the range of possibility, that each one of us
who lives a full lifetime may actually perceive,
such an ideal can spur and fire the imagination,
not only of our own nation, but of the world.
It is my prayer that I may present such a racial
ideal, not only to my own people but to humanity.
It is my prayer that I may live to see in the generation of my grandchildren a humanity from which
almost all the most blackening and distressing
elements have been eliminated, and in which
the vernal bodily beauty and unsullied spiritual
power of those then growing up will surpass
anything that we know to-day except among
the rare and gifted few. This is not a wild
dream ; it is a real potentiality almost within
reach. The materialization of this vital racial
vision is in the hands of the mothers for the
next twenty or thirty years.

If every woman will but consciously and deliberately exercise the powers of her motherhood
after learning of those powers ; if she bear

only those children which she and her mate ardently desire ; if she refuse to bear any but these, and if she so space these children that she herself rests and recovers vitality between their births, and during their coming she lives in such a way as I have indicated in the preceding chapters, and if at the same time the deadly and horrible scourges of the venereal diseases and the multitude of ramifications of racial baseness are eliminated *as they can be*, then with a comparatively small percentage of accidents and unforeseeable errors, the quality of those born will enormously improve, and by a second generation all should be already far on the highway to new and wonderful powers, which are to-day almost unsuspected.

What are the greatest dangers which jeopardize the materialization of this glorious dream of a human stock represented only by well-formed, desired, well-endowed beautiful men and women ? Two main dangers are in the way of its consummation ; the first is ignorance It is difficult to reach the untutored mind, to teach a public hardened and deadened to callousness and the lack of dreams of their own ; even though if one could but reach them it would be possible to make them understand.

A second and almost greater danger is not a simple ignorance, but the inborn incapacity which lies in the vast and ever increasing stock of degenerate, feeble-minded and unbalanced who are now in our midst and who devastate social customs. These populate most rapidly, these tend proportionately to increase, and these are like the parasite upon the healthy tree sapping its vitality. These produce less than they consume and are able only to flourish and reproduce so long as the healthier produce food for them ; but by ever weakening the human stock, in the end they will succumb with the fine structure which they have destroyed.

There appear then two obstacles which might block the materialization of my racial vision ; on the one hand the ignorance of those who have latent powers. This only needs to be stirred by knowledge and the inspiration of an ideal, to become potent. This obstacle is not unsurmountable. If one but speaks in sufficiently burning words, if one but writes sufficiently contagiously, the ideas must spread with ever increasing acceleration. Ignorance must be vanquished by winged knowledge. I hold it to be the duty of the dreamer of great dreams not only to express them in such a way that cognate souls may also perceive them. It is the duty of a seer to embody his message in such a form that its beauty is apparent and the vision can be seen by all the people. The infectiousness of disease, the contagion of destructive and horrible bacterial germs have become a commonplace in our social consciousness, and we have forgotten, and our artists have in recent years tended ever more and more to forget that the highest form of art should also be infectious. Goodness, beauty and prophetic vision have as strong a contagious quality as disease if they are embodied in a form rendered vital by the mating of truth and beauty

To overcome mere ignorance in others is, therefore, by no means a hopeless task, and it is the valiant work of the artist-prophet. Youth is the time to catch the contagion of goodness. To youth I appeal.

The other obstacle presents a deeper and more difficult task. It must deal with the terrible debasing power of the inferior, the depraved and feeble-minded, to whom reason means nothing and can mean nothing, who are thriftless, unmanageable and appallingly prolific. Yet if the good in our race is not to be swamped and destroyed by the debased as the fine tree by the parasite, this prolific depravity must be curbed. How shall this be done ? A very few quite simple Acts of Parliament could deal with it.

Three short and concise Bills would be sufficient to afford the most urgent social service for the preservation of our race. They should be simply worded and based on possibilities well within the grasp of modern science.

The idea of sterilization has not yet been very

generally understood or accepted, although it is an idea which our civilization urgently needs to assimilate. I think that a large part of the objections to it, often made passionately and eloquently by those from whom one would otherwise have expected a more intelligent attitude, is due to complete ignorance of the facts. Even otherwise instructed persons confuse sterilization with castration. The arguments which to-day in a chance discussion of the subject are always brought forward against sterilization have been, in my experience, only those which apply to castration. To castrate any male is, of course, not only to deprive him of his manhood and thus to injure his personal consciousness, but to remove bodily organs, the loss of which adversely affects his mentality and which will also affect the internal secretions which have a profound influence on his whole organization. I fully endorse the views of the opponents of this process.

It is, however, neither necessary to castrate nor is it suggested by those who, like myself, would like to see the sterilization of those totally unfit for parenthood made an immediate possibility, indeed made compulsory. As Dr. Havelock Ellis stated in an article in the *Eugenics Review*, Vol. I, No. 3, October 1909, pp. 203-206, sterilization under proper conditions is a very different and much simpler matter and one which has no deleterious and far reaching effects on the whole system. The operation is trivial, scarcely painful, and does not debar the subject from experiencing all his normal reaction in ordinary union ; it only prevents the procreation of children.

It has been found in some States of America, and as I know from private correspondents in this country, there are men who would welcome the relief from the ever present anxiety of potential parenthood which they know full well would be ruinous to the future generation.

There is also the possibility of sterilization by the direct action of " X " rays. At present sterility is known as an unfortunate danger to those engaged in scientific research with radium, but it might, under control, be wisely used as a painless method of sterilization. This may prove of particular value for women in whom the operation corresponding to the severance of the ducts of the man is more serious. It appears however, not always to be permanent in its effect. In some circumstances this may be an advantage, in others a disadvantage.

With reference to the sterilizing effect of " X "-rays, the following quotation from F. H. Marshall, *The Physiology of Reproduction*, 1910, is pertinent :—

A more special cause of sterility in men is one which operates in the case of workers with radium or the Röntgen rays. Several years ago Albers-Schönberg noticed that the X-rays induced sterility in guinea pigs and rabbits, but without interfering with the sexual potency. These observations have been confirmed by other investigators, who have shown, further, that the azoöspermia is due to the degeneration of the cells lining the seminal canals. In men it has been proved that mere presence in an X-ray atmosphere incidental to radiography sooner or later causes a condition of complete sterility, but without any apparent diminution of sexual potency. As Gordon observes, for those working in an X-ray atmosphere adequate protection for all parts of the body not directly exposed for examination or treatment is indispensable, but, on the other hand, the X-rays afford a convenient, painless and harmless method of inducing sterility, in cases in which it is desirable to effect this result.

When Bills are passed to ensure the sterility of the hopelessly rotten and racially diseased, and to provide for the education of the child-bearing woman so that she spaces her children healthily, our race will rapidly quell the stream of depraved, hopeless and wretched lives which are at present ever increasing in proportion in our midst. Before this stream at present the thoughtful shrink but do nothing. Such action as will be possible when these bills are passed will not only increase the relative *proportion* of the sound and healthy among us who may consciously contribute to the higher and more beautiful forms of the human race, but by the elimination of wasteful lives which are to-day seldom self-supporting, and which are so largely the cause of the cost and outlay of public money in their institutional treatment and their partial relief, will check an increasing drain on our national resources. The setting free of this public money would make it possible for those now too heavily taxed to reproduce their own and more valuable kinds.

The miserable, the degenerate, the utterly wretched in body and mind, who when reproducing multiply the misery and evil of the world, would be the first to be thankful for the escape such legislation would offer from the wretchedness entailed not only on their offspring but on themselves. The Labour Party, all Progressives, and all Conservatives who desire to conserve the good can unite to support measures so directly calculated to improve the physical condition, the mental happiness and the general well-being of the human race.

Even to-day almost all the thriftiest and better of the working class, and the artisan class in particular, are already in the ranks of those who are sponged upon, and to some extent taxed, for the upkeep of the incompetent, and it is just from among the best artisan and from the middle class that the most serious minded parents and those who recognize their racial responsibilities are principally to be found. There is throughout the whole Labour movement, as throughout the less vocal but deeper feeling of the middle class, a passionate desire to eliminate the misery and human degradation which on every hand to-day saddens the tender conscience. The limiting of their own families to meet the pressure of circumstances will never achieve their desires. The best to-day are making less and less headway, and the inferior are increasing more and more in proportion to them.

Directly, however, the need for such legislation as I have outlined above is realized, and such legislation is passed, then the tide will be turned. Then, at last, we shall begin to see the elimination of the horror and degradation of humanity, which at present is apparently so hopeless and permanent a blot upon the world. And then, and then at once, will the positive effects of the conscious working of love and beauty and desired motherhood begin to take effect. The evolution of humanity will take a leap forward when we have around us only fine and beautiful young people, all of whom have been conceived, carried and born in true homes by conscious, powerful and voluntary mothers.

Meanwhile the prison reformers, psychoanalysts, doctors, teachers and reformers of all sorts will be going on with their reforms, and will be claiming this and that wonderful improvement in the school children, and they will probably never realize that it will not be their reforms which have worked these apparent miracles ; it will be the change in the attitude of the mother, the return to the position of power of the mother, her voluntary motherhood, the conscious and deliberate creation by the mother and her mate of the fine and splendid race which to-day, as God's prophet, I see in a vision and which might so speedily be materialized on earth.

APPENDICES

A. PHYSICAL SIGNS OF COMING MOTHER-
   HOOD.

B. ON BIRTH.

C. SUGGESTIONS FOR CALCULATING DATE
   OF ANTICIPATED BIRTH.

APPENDIX A

Physical Signs of Coming Motherhood

Sometimes a woman is doubtful whether or not she is about to become a mother, and may be too shy to ask those with whom she is associated. She should, if it is possible, seek the advice of a highly qualified midwife or medical practitioner, but this is not always possible, and it may be useful for her to know the following signs :—

The first and most widely recognized indication that conception has taken place is "missing a period" or the cessation of the menstrual flow, while, at the same time, there is no ill-health. A woman may even feel unusually bright and well.

There is generally an increase in the size of the breast, followed as the months progress by a very noticeable increase in the size and bright blue colour of the veins round the breast, and also a darkening in colour and a changing from pink to brownish tint of the area round the centre of the breast.

After the third month, there is visible a steadily increasing enlargement of the lower part of the body, but, as this also happens with some forms of illness, this alone and without the other signs is not proof that motherhood has commenced.

"Quickening" or the movements of the child, are a much better indication of motherhood, and these are generally to be perceived about the twentieth week, or roughly half-way through the whole period of prenatal life; but see further the remarks in Chapter XIII, p. 113.

The perception of the child's heart beats is absolute proof of coming motherhood. These may be perceived after the fourth or fifth month quite readily by a nurse or other observer, though the mother herself can but seldom perceive them.

"Morning Sickness," which is so often experienced, and in most books for the "expectant mother" is quoted as one of the first signs of pregnancy, *should never occur at all*—see Chapter XI—although unfortunately it is true that it does frequently occur in women who are bearing children under present conditions.

Sometimes, though rarely, a birth is unexpected, but these cases are so unusual as to cause no anxiety in normal circumstances. Such a rare and curious case as a totally unexpected birth is recorded in the *Lancet* for September 1922.

APPENDIX B

On Birth

The usual agonies of child birth vary greatly in extent according to the structure of the woman. But, as was shown in Chapter II, the tendency already is present, and probably will increase, for this to be an almost intolerable strain upon the woman. Tardily indeed have efforts to relieve her agonies in child birth been made; Queen Victoria took a grave and adventurous step when she bore one of her children under chloroform. Chloroform, however, only deadens consciousness at a comparatively late stage in child birth, and its use through the many long hours, even perhaps sometimes days of agony which precede the later stages is not often possible. It is, therefore, for some types of women a very insufficient narcotic.

Natural " painless Child Birth " is, of course, the ideal, and is claimed to be the result of the " fruit and rice diet," see *Tokology* by Dr. Alice Stockham, but although this greatly reduces the pain for many, and undoubtedly makes the months of pregnancy easier, it cannot make birth anything but a torture if the proportion of the child's head to the bony arch is above a given limit. The "Christian Science" claim for not only painless but bloodless birth has been reported to me, but never at first hand, and I have not yet had the first-hand statements of women who are said to have experienced it.

"Twilight Sleep," a comparatively recent discovery, has been much advocated, much praised and much blamed. There may be types of women who find it advantageous, but the fact that it necessitates going to a nursing home, away from home, is very much against its use under ideal circumstances. For those who have no home, or a sordid and overcrowded one, a nursing home may be a place of refuge. "Twilight Sleep" (scopolamine-morphine) is, however, for the more sensitive type of woman, an extremely unreliable drug, which may frequently take no narcotic effect upon the patient, who suffers added agony as the result of relying upon it, and it may be very dangerous for the child.

There is also the method of birth through the soft part of the body, avoiding the birth of the child through the bony structure altogether. This operation is described as Cesarean section, and involves incision both through the abdominal walls and through the walls of the womb. For some women with very small bones Cesarean section is necessary if they are to produce living children. Even for women who, by paying the price of agony, can produce children by normal birth, this method may be found very advantageous. I see a possibility of its widely extended future use. In hundreds, perhaps thousands of years hence when the child's head will be proportionately even larger in comparison with the mother's bones than it is to-day, it may indeed be the only method which will stand between the higher human races and their total extinction.

While pregnancy and birth are as a rule conspicuous phenomena about which there is no mistake, in a few cases they may be going on without the mother herself being conscious! An extreme case was reported in the *British Medical Journal* in 1922 of a woman who was pregnant without knowing it, and to whom a child was born in a few moments although she was quite unaware that she was about to be a mother. And I know personally of a few other cases where medical practitioners have attended women for the birth of infants that they only realised at the last moment were about to be born. Any such case is of interest, and perhaps to some people might indicate an ideal state of affairs. I do not know of any careful investigation of the individuals who have had such births, and suspect that they would prove to have very large pelvic bones. Sometimes such cases illustrate also another unusual feature of pregnancy, that is the continuation of the menstrual period all through the period of pregnancy. As a rule of course menstruation ceases at the first month after conception, and is generally the first sign to a woman that she is about to become a mother, but though it is uncommon, it should be known to women that menstruation may, and sometimes does, persist through pregnancy.

There is a certain amount of rather gossipy opinion that women who are spared the full torture of child birth do not have equally passionate love for the child. This, however, is nonsense. Love depends far more on the mother's desire for parenthood at the time of the child's conception and her feelings towards it all through the months of waiting than on the hours of birth, although the appealing weakness and fascination of a baby may win a deeper love than the mother-to-be expected to feel for her child.

APPENDIX C

The leading authority in the *Manual of Human Embryology*,
edited by Franz, Keibel and Franklin P. Mall in two volumes,
London, 1910, says:—

> "In ancient times it was generally believed that the
> duration of pregnancy in man, unlike that in lower animals,
> was of very uncertain length; and it was not until the
> seventeenth century that it was more accurately fixed,
> by Fidele of Palermo, at forty weeks, counting from the
> last menstrual period. In the next century Haller found
> that if pregnancy is reckoned from the time of a fruitful
> copulation it is usually thirty-nine weeks, and rarely forty
> weeks in duration. In general these results are fully
> confirmed by the thousands of careful data collected
> during the nineteenth century."

.   .   .   .   .

> "However, from thousands of records it is found
> that the mean duration of a pregnancy varies in first and
> second pregnancies, is more protracted in healthy women,
> in married women, in winter, and in the upper classes."

.   .   .   .   .

> "From these figures it is seen that most pregnancies
> take place during the first week after menstruation, and

that the duration of pregnancy is longer if copulation takes place towards the end of the intermenstrual period. And this is explained if we assume that in the first week, especially the first few days after the cessation of menstruation, the ovum is in the upper end of the tube awaiting the sperm and that conception immediately follows copulation. When the fruitful copulation takes place in the latter two weeks of the month the opposite is usually the case; the sperm wanders to the ovary and there awaits the ovum; and, therefore, on an average, pregnancy is prolonged in this group of cases, when determined from the time of copulation."

.   .   .   .

"In determining the age of human embryos it is probably more nearly correct to count from the *end* of the last period, for all evidence points to that time as the most probable at which pregnancy takes place."

.   .   .   .

On the whole it is generally found that 280 days (*i.e.*, 40 weeks) can be reckoned as the average period during which the child develops internally if the date is counted from the first day of the last menstrual period and 269 days if estimated from the date of actual union.

Leuckart tabulated results from a large number of births which took place within the first ten months of marriage, and found that there was a maximum number of births on the 275th day, then a decrease and a second maximum on the 293rd day. Nevertheless, in spite of careful reckoning, there are, as will be recognized, many sources of error, and medical men and nurses are often wisely cautious of giving any exact date for an anticipated birth; sometimes too cautious even to suggest the week within which the birth will take place.

I have known a good many mothers, however, who were much more accurately certain about this point than their attendants, and have found that the birth took place exactly on the day they anticipated. As an illustration of this, I give the answer from one of my correspondents, both of whose children were born on the exact day she anticipated. I asked her how she estimated these periods, and she said :—

" I simply took old Dr. Chevasse's rule which he gives in *Advice to a Wife*; you know how he puts the date of conception and opposite it the probable date of birth. I went by the first union after the last period. It so happened that my husband was seedy and there was no union for a fortnight after the end of the period. I took that first union as the date of conception and looking up the date in Chevasse and the corresponding date of birth opposite, I found it to be August 20th, and sure enough on August 20th he was born. With the second boy, the union took place the day after the last period, and I took that as the starting date and against it I found January 21st and on January 21st he arrived in spite of the doctors insisting in each case that it would be three weeks earlier. What I do is, I always make a mark in my diary against the date of first union after every period. Then when I had missed a period and so knew that there was probably conception, I could at once tell the probable date."

The table Chevasse quoted from Galabin is as follows —

From					
Jan. 1st to Oct. 1st = 273 (274) days,	add	5 (4) days
„ Feb. 1st to Nov. 1st = 273 (274) „	„	5 (4) „
„ Mar. 1st to Dec. 1st = 275 „	„	3 „
„ Apl. 1st to Jan. 1st = 275 „	„	3 „
„ May 1st to Feb. 1st = 276 „	„	2 „

From June 1st to Mar. 1st = 273 (274) days, add 5 (4) days
  „   July 1st to Apl. 1st = 274 (275) „   „ 4 (3) „
  „   Aug. 1st to May 1st = 273 (274) „   „ 5 (4) „
  „   Sep. 1st to June 1st = 273 (274) „   „ 5 (4) „
  „   Oct. 1st to July 1st = 273 (274) „   „ 5 (4) „
  „   Nov. 1st to Aug. 1st = 273 (274) „   „ 5 (4) „
  „   Dec. 1st to Sep. 1st = 274 (275) „   „ 4 (3) „

Printed in Great Britain by
UNWIN BROTHERS, LIMITED, THE GRESHAM PRESS   LONDON AND WOKING

EIGHTEENTH EDITION, REVISED AND ENLARGED

MARRIED LOVE

A NEW CONTRIBUTION TO THE SOLUTION OF SEX DIFFICULTIES,

By MARIE CARMICHAEL STOPES, D.Sc., Ph.D.

SIX SHILLINGS NET (Postage 4d.)

" Dr. Marie Stopes has endeavoured to meet the need of healthy young people of the educated class for information as to the sexual responsibilities of marriage. Though not a medical woman, the author has special qualifications for this task ; with high scientific attainments she combines literary skill, sympathetic insight, idealism, and more than common courage. . . . To the married and to those about to marry, provided they are normal in mind and body and not afraid of facing facts, this should prove a most helpful book."—*British Medical Journal.*

" Like all Dr. Stopes's writing, it is clear, thoughtful, penetrating, and undoubtedly is a scientific contribution towards a subject which a decade ago would have been taboo. . . . Our advice is for women to read it and for men to read it, for there is here stated a real problem which is specifically English."—*English Review.*

" In saying that, unless the art of love is studied, marriage cannot bear its full fruits, she sees, as the greatest thinkers have always seen, that marriage is a symbol of transcendental significance. . . . In exquisite quality of understanding the book is a contribution to its subject, which in time will receive the recognition that it deserves."—*The Hospital.*

" It is probably the most important contribution to the sex problem that has ever been made really *accessible* to the English public."—*Cambridge Magazine.*

" This is a remarkable book which gives much information regarding the physiology of marital life. . . . All medical men and medical women should read and study this book. They cannot fail to glean from its pages valuable information."—*Medical Times.*

G. P. PUTNAM'S SONS, LTD.

24 BEDFORD STREET, STRAND, LONDON, W.C. 2

FOURTEENTH EDITION, REVISED AND ENLARGED

WISE PARENTHOOD

A PRACTICAL SEQUEL TO "MARRIED LOVE"
A HANDBOOK ON BIRTH CONTROL

By MARIE CARMICHAEL STOPES, D.Sc., Ph.D.

THREE SHILLINGS AND SIXPENCE NET (Postage 3d.)

As not only individual enquirers, but the world at large, and even the medical profession, lack a rational, scientific and critical consideration of the effects of the birth-control methods now used by millions of people, this little book seems urgently needed. It is hoped that it will help materially to improve our race and to check the spread of nervous and other injuries so prevalent as a result of ignorant attempts to obtain that wise and health-giving control of parenthood which all who think must crave.

"I would strongly recommend any who are interested in the practical aspect [the scientific method of birth control] to read a little book which has just appeared, from the pen of Dr. Marie C. Stopes, 'Wise Parenthood.'"—C. KILLICK MILLARD (Medical Officer of Health for Leicester) in *Medical Officer*, December 7, 1918.

"The method is that which people, including many doctors, want to know. . . . It meets the immense æsthetic difficulties. . . . The work is especially for those happy people who recognize the kindred duty and delight of having, by a healthy mother, healthy children. The wretches who wish to avoid all children are punished as only great offenders are punished, by the fulfilment of their desire. This little book, however, may show them the risks which they are incurring."—*The Hospital.*

"The author ably presents the case for birth control from the scientific point of view. She criticizes several of the more important birth control methods at present employed, and she gives a detailed description of a method which she considers reliable and safe. . . . No medical man or medical woman should fail to secure a copy and read it carefully."—*Medical Times*, December, 1918.

G. P. PUTNAM'S SONS, LTD.

24 BEDFORD STREET, STRAND, LONDON, W.C. 2

CONTRACEPTION

(BIRTH CONTROL)

ITS THEORY, HISTORY AND PRACTICE

A Manual for the Medical and Legal Professions

BY

MARIE CARMICHAEL STOPES, D.Sc., Ph.D.

Fellow of University College, London.

With Introduction by Prof. Sir William Bayliss, F.R.S.;
Introductory Notes by Sir James Barr, M.D.,
Christopher Rolleston, M.D., Dr. Jane
Hawthorne and "Obscurus."

Price 12/6 net.

CONTENTS

This book is the first manual on the subject, and is packed with both helpful and interesting matter, and much that is new and noteworthy.

Sir WILLIAM BAYLISS says : "It cannot fail to be of real service."

Dr. ROLLESTON says : "I predict a great success for the work, and I wish to record my thanks to the author for her pioneer work in preventive medicine."

THE MEDICAL TIMES says : "The book is unique, and marks a new era."

Order from your Bookseller or direct from the Publishers :

JOHN BALE, SONS & DANIELSSON, LTD.
83-91, GREAT TITCHFIELD STREET, LONDON, W. I.

THE CONTROL
OF PARENTHOOD

BY

Prof. J. ARTHUR THOMSON, M.A., LL.D.

Prof. LEONARD HILL, M.B., F.R.S.

The Very Rev. DEAN INGE, C.V.O., D.D.

Mr. HAROLD COX (Editor *Edinburgh Review*)

Dr. MARY SCHARLIEB, C.B.E., M.D., M.S.

Sir RIDER HAGGARD, K.B.E.

Rev. Principal A. E. GARVIE, M.A., D.D.

Rev. F. B. MEYER, B.A., D.D.

Dr. MARIE STOPES, D.Sc., Ph.D., F.L.S.

Introduction by The BISHOP OF BIRMINGHAM

EDITED BY

Rev. Sir JAMES MARCHANT, K.B.E., LL.D., F.L.S., F.R.S.Ed.

SECRETARY OF THE NATIONAL BIRTH-RATE COMMISSION, ETC.

Crown 8vo. Cloth. 6s. net (Postage, 4d.)

AT ALL BOOKSELLERS

In this book a group of distinguished scientists, economists, and leaders of religious thought, give their frank opinions on the reduction of population and on birth control.

" . . . It is time there was some plain speaking on this all-important matter, and nothing could be franker, and fuller, or more to the purpose than these papers by the highest religious, social, scientific and economic authorities."—*Truth.*

G. P. PUTNAM'S SONS, LTD.

24 BEDFORD STREET, STRAND, LONDON, W.C.2

Books by ELLEN KEY

"All of Ellen Key's books display an astonishing amount of reading, of experience, and of thought. Best and deepest and rarest of all in Ellen Key is the entire absence of any bitterness in her composition. The reader will find in her books a deeper and higher vision of womanhood, of eugenics, of the divinity and destiny of life, than any other pages of our time. . . . The wisest woman in the world."—Dr. C. W. SALEEBY in *Pall Mall Gazette*.

LOVE
AND MARRIAGE

WITH A CRITICAL AND BIOGRAPHICAL INTRODUCTION BY HAVELOCK ELLIS

Crown 8vo. Cloth. 10s. net (Postage 4 d.)

"The author is absolutely in earnest, has thought deeply on her subject, and has therefore written so as to interest."—*Pall Mall Gazette*.

G. P. PUTNAM'S SONS, LTD.
24 BEDFORD STREET, STRAND, LONDON, W.C. 2

Books by ELLEN KEY

THE RENAISSANCE OF MOTHERHOOD

Crown 8vo. Cloth. 7s. 6d. *net (Postage, 4d.)*

IN this volume, the author of "Love and Marriage" considers certain problems connected with women's most important mission. She calls the attention of an age that is the victim of divergent interests to the ancient claim of the child upon the mother, a claim that represents the most elemental of altruistic bonds. Ellen Key points out that motherhood and the care of children is woman's prerogative, and that the division of labour between the sexes is a natural one. An interesting suggestion toward the solution of certain social problems is made in the form of a proposed subsidizing of motherhood.

G. P. PUTNAM'S SONS, LTD.

24 BEDFORD STREET, STRAND, LONDON, W.C. 2

Books by ELLEN KEY

THE CENTURY OF THE CHILD

Crown 8vo. Cloth. 12s. net (Postage 4d.)

CONTENTS : The Right of the Child to Choose His
Parents, The Unborn Race and Woman's Work, Education, Homelessness, Soul Murder in the Schools, The School
of the Future, Religious Instruction, Child Labour and the
Crimes of Children. This book has gone through more
than twenty German Editions and has been published in
several European countries.

"The book is significant of the unrest and the search towards new
ideals which are making themselves felt in so many ways and in so
many countries."—*Manchester Guardian.*

"A profound and analytical discussion by a great Scandinavian
teacher, of the reasons why modern education does not better educate."—*Christian Herald.*

THE EDUCATION OF THE CHILD

Reprinted from the Authorized American Edition of
The Century of the Child. With Introductory Note by
EDWARD BOK

Crown 8vo. Cloth. 5s. net (Postage, 4d.)

"Nothing finer on the wise education of the child has ever been
brought into print. To me this chapter is a perfect classic ; it points
the way straight for every parent, and it should find a place in every
home in America where there is a child."—EDWARD BOK, Editor of
the *Ladies' Home Journal.*

"This book, by one of the most thoughtful students of child life
among current writers, is one that will prove invaluable to parents who
desire to develop in their children that strength of character, self-
control and personality that alone makes for a well-rounded, useful and
happy life."—*Baltimore Sun.*

G. P. PUTNAM'S SONS, LTD.
24 BEDFORD STREET, STRAND, LONDON, W.C.2

THE CORNER-STONE OF EDUCATION

AN ESSAY ON THE HOME-TRAINING OF CHILDREN

By EDWARD LYTTELTON, D.D.
LATE HEADMASTER OF ETON

Crown 8vo. Cloth. 7s. 6d. net. (*Postage, 4 d.*)

CONTENTS

G. P. PUTNAM'S SONS, LTD.
24 BEDFORD STREET, STRAND, LONDON, W.C. 2